The EQUUS Illustrated

Handbook of Equine Anatomy

The Musculoskeletal System:
Anatomy of Movement
and Locomotion

By Susan E. Hakola, B.S., R.N., C.M.I.
and Ronald J. Riegel, D.V.M.

First Published in 2006 by PRIMEDIA Equine Network

PRIMEDIA Equine Network / EQUUS Magazine
656 Quince Orchard Road, #600
Gaithersburg, MD 20878
301-977-3900

VP, Group Publishing Director: Susan Harding
Director, Product Marketing: Julie Beaulieu

Cover Photo - Darrell Dodds
Cover Illustration - Susan E. Hakola
Back Cover Illustrations - Susan E. Hakola, Andrea O'Shea
Book Design - Susan E. Hakola

Order by calling **800-952-5813** or online at **www.HorseBooksEtc.com**

Library of Congress Cataloging-in-Publication Data

Hakola, Susan E.
  The Equus illustrated handbook of equine anatomy : the musculoskeletal
system : the anatomy of movement and locomotion / by Susan E. Hakola and
Ronald J. Riegel.
    p. cm.
  ISBN-13: 978-1-929164-33-2
  ISBN-10: 1-929164-33-5
  1. Horses--Anatomy--Atlases. 2. Musculoskeletal system--Anatomy--Atlases.
I. Riegel, Ronald J. II. Title.

  SF765.H35 2006
  636.1089'17--dc22

Printed in Colombia

2006018099

TABLE OF CONTENTS

TABLE OF CONTENTS

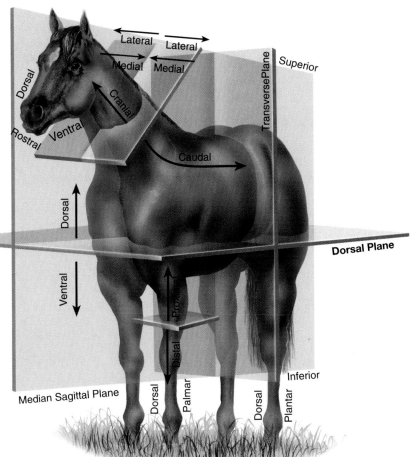

SUSAN HAKOLA / J. DIRIG

Directional Terms

Anterior vs. Posterior: Anterior literally means "in front of" whereas posterior means "in back of."

Ventral vs. Dorsal: Ventral structures lie towards the belly of the animal. Dorsal structures lie towards the back.

Superior vs. Inferior: Superior refers to any area towards the head, whereas inferior refers to any area towards the feet.

Cranial vs. Caudal: Cranially means relatively towards the head and caudally means towards the tail. In regards to the cranium itself, any thing towards the muzzle is referred to as being **rostral**.

Medial vs. Lateral: Structures that lie medially are said to lie towards the medial or midline plane. Those that lie towards the flank or side of the animal are said to lie laterally.

Proximal vs. Distal: These terms have specific application to the limbs. Those structures that lie proximally occur nearest to the trunk of the body. Those positioned distally lie furthest away from the body.

Palmar vs. Plantar: With respect to the limbs, the palmar surface refers to the back of the forelimb and plantar refers to the back of the hindlimb.

Adaxial vs. Abaxial: Adaxial refers to structures occurring towards the axis of the body whereas abaxial refers to the distancing of structures away from the main axis of the body.

External vs. Internal: Externally refers to all that is referenced outside of the body and internally is all that is within.

Superficial vs. Deep: Structures that occur towards the surface of the skin are referred to as the superficial structures whereas deep structures refer to those found beneath the surface.

Anatomical Planes

There are three main planes of reference that allows one to view structural relationships in the anatomical position. The median plane divides the animal symmetrically into right and left halves. Any plane parallel to the median plane is referred to as a sagittal plane. A dorsal plane can be one of any number of parallel planes that divides the body symmetrically dorsally and ventrally. The transverse planes transect any anatomical part, i.e. the neck or a limb, perpendicularly to its own long axis.

The Structure Of Bone

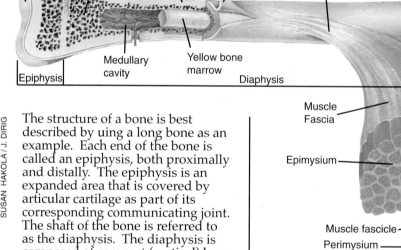

Articular cartilage · Cancellous bone · Cortical bone · Periosteum · Tendon · Articular cartilage · Epiphysis · Medullary cavity · Yellow bone marrow · Diaphysis · Muscle Fascia · Epimysium · Muscle fascicle · Perimysium · Cell membrane · Endomysium · Muscle fiber · Nucleus · Myofibril

SUSAN HAKOLA / J. DIRIG

The structure of a bone is best described by uing a long bone as an example. Each end of the bone is called an epiphysis, both proximally and distally. The epiphysis is an expanded area that is covered by articular cartilage as part of its corresponding communicating joint. The shaft of the bone is referred to as the diaphysis. The diaphysis is composed of compact (cortical) bone versus the spongy bone (or cancellous bone) that comprises the epiphysis. Trabeculae, which are a honey comb of branching bony plates, are the building blocks of the spongy bone.

The tough fibrous connective tissue that covers the entire bone except for the articular cartilage is called the periosteum. The fibers from the tendons and ligaments communicate continuously with the fibers of the periosteum and facilitate their attachment to the bone. Each bone in the skeletal system is composed of compact and spongy bone. In specific cases, spongy bone is covered by compact bone or plates of compact bone. The medullary cavity is the hollow chamber present within the areas surrounded by compact bone. This area is lined with a thin layer of squamous cells that is called the endosteum and filled with connective tissue called marrow.

The periosteal and medullary arteries provide the vascular supply to the long bones. The periosteum is supplied by the periosteal artery which branches into minute arterioles that enter the compact bone through very small openings. The medullary artery enters the long bone through the nutrient foramena within the compact bone and anastomoses with the vasculature of the bone marrow. The venous drainage occurs almost entirely near the articular surfaces.

The Synovial Joint

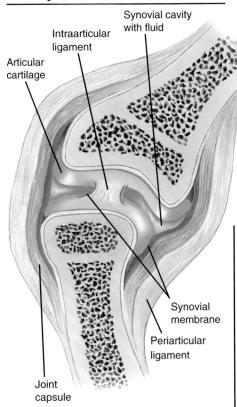

Synovial cavity with fluid

Intraarticular ligament

Articular cartilage

Synovial membrane

Periarticular ligament

Joint capsule

SUSAN HAKOLA / J. DIRIG

The cancellous-containing epiphysis is covered with a layer of hyaline cartilage that is referred to as articular cartilage. This hyaline cartilage is smooth, resistant to wear, and varies in depth depending on the anatomical area. The joint capsule is in reality a tube that holds the two bones together and is composed of two distinct layers. The outer layer is fibrous, dense and anastomoses with the periosteal membrane of the bone. Collagenous fibers called ligaments help reinforce this joint capsule and prevent excessive movement within the joint.

The inner layer of the joint capsule is vascular and is comprised of loose connective tissue. This is referred to as the synovial membrane. This membrane covers the entire area of the joint except for those areas covered by the articular cartilage. The synovium forms the boundary of the synovial or articular cavity. This cavity is filled with a thick, yellow-tinged, lubricating fluid that is secreted by the synovial membrane and is commonly called the synovial fluid. Some synovial joints also contain small, closed fluid-filled sacs referred to as bursa.

Ligaments

Ligaments are composed of strong, inelastic fibrous tissue which travel from bone to bone. They fall into two categories of periarticular and intraarticular. Collateral ligaments are examples of periarticular ligaments. They are distinct in structure, located both outside and within the fibrous joint capsule. Periarticular ligaments aid in controlling the range of motion within that particular joint. The intraarticular ligaments connect bone to bone and have the synovial membrane reflected over them.

Anatomy of a Tendon

Dense white fibrous tissue surrounds each muscle bundle and ends in a cord-like tissue commonly called a tendon. The fibers of a tendon weave into the fibers comprising the periosteum, resulting in the attachment of muscles to bones. These bands of fibrous tissue vary in size, dependent on the size of the muscle, the area of attachment, and the mechanical requirements of that anatomical area.

Tendons are remarkable in that they possess great strength, elasticity and the capacity of storing energy when stretched. The strength of the tendon tissue is found within its anatomical structure. Collagen fibrils lying in longitudinal orientation surrounded by fibroblasts form the basic tendon bundle. This tendon unit forms larger secondary bundles referred to as fascicles. These secondary bundles form larger bundles that create a helical pattern within the tendon. The strength of the entire tendon evolves from this interwoven helical structure.

The tendon tissue is oriented longitudinally. The fibrils and bundles run parallel to each other. Since most of these elastic structures are under constant stress and strain, it is important that these tissues are renewable. The fibroblastic cells renew all of the collagen every six months as the fibrils are replaced.

The tendon structure facilitates the transmission of force from muscle to bone. In order to do this, it must be able to move easily over its surrounding structures. This ability to glide is possible due to the surrounding structures of the tendon sheath, bursae, and paratendons.

A tendon sheath is formed whenever the tendon changes direction in an abrupt fashion, such as crossing a joint. An outer fibrous sheath and an inner synovial lining comprise the structure of the tendon sheath. This forms a circumscribed cavity containing synovial fluid.

Bursa sacs are located wherever a tendon passes over a bony prominence and prevent injury to the tendinous tissues when they travel over osseous structures. They differ from tendon sheaths in that bursae usually do not completely circumscribe the entire tendon. These sacs of fluid may be located just between the tendon and bone or can occassionally occur around the entire circumference completely enclosing it within the tendon sheath.

When a tendon is asked to travel a straight course, and a tendon sheath is not required, the surrounding structure is referred to as a paratendon. This structure is composed of loosely arranged areolar tissue that allows gliding function when a tendon sheath is not present.

Excessive tension is more likely to cause detachment or a tear in the muscle than to injure the tendon itself. The elastic recoil of the tendon contributes to locomotion. A percentage of the metabolic work performed by muscles causes the tendons to stretch which results in the release of stored energy at a later time.

The Skeletal Muscles

The basic cellular unit of the equine muscle is the muscle fiber. Each one of these units responds to a stimulation by contracting and then relaxing. These muscle fiber cells contain a cell membrane and cytoplasm which contains many nuclei and mitochondria. Within its' cytoplasm lies numerous threadlike myofibrils that lie in parallel bundles. Two types of protein, actin and myosin, exist within the myofibrils. These protein structures produce the characteristic striations of light and dark areas within the muscle fiber.

SUSAN HAKOLA

The Skeleton and The Joints

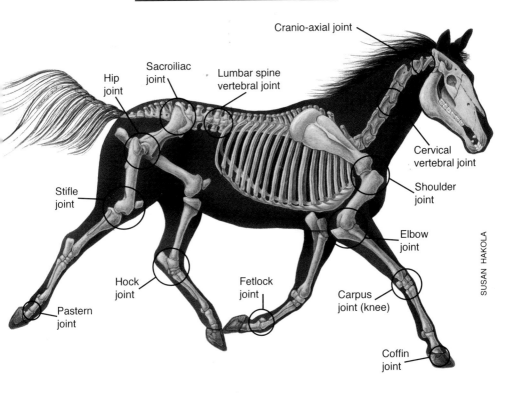

Cranio-axial joint

Sacroiliac joint

Hip joint

Lumbar spine vertebral joint

Cervical vertebral joint

Stifle joint

Shoulder joint

Elbow joint

Hock joint

Fetlock joint

Carpus joint (knee)

Pastern joint

Coffin joint

SUSAN HAKOLA

Biomechanics of Locomotion

Inherently, the flight response of the horse is quite strong. The horse runs first and then turns to contemplate the excitatory stimulus. Those equids that could not escape to point B from point A were not selected for their other inherent function in life, that of reproduction. What made this locomotion possible is the musculoskeletal system governed by both the central and peripheral nervous systems.

The musculoskeletal system is composed of components similar to that of a simple machine. The skeletal system serves as the framework. The joints serve as connectors, shock absorbers or linkages, the tendons and ligaments serve as cords and connectors, and the muscles serve as the source of energy. The resulting work of this simple, yet complex machine is to move this mass

of horse from one point to another.

Dorsal

Ventral

SUSAN HAKOLA / J. DIRIG

This biomechanical machine, like any other machine, must be in balance between the mass of the animal and its supporting structures. Regardless of the breed, the entire body of the horse can be divided into three equal parts. An axis drawn from the point of the shoulder to the center of the stifle and parallel to the ground should divide the animal equally dorsally and ventrally. A perpendicular axis from the withers distally to this horizontal axis, and one from the cranial aspect of the tuber coxae distally to just anterior to the stifle will divide the animal into three equal parts. The median plane, when viewed dorsally, will divide the body equally into right and left halves.

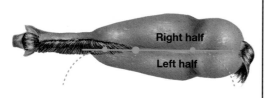

Right half
Left half

The center of gravity for the horse depends on the shape and the motion that is being performed. The forelimbs are forced to bear 60 - 65% of the horse's weight. This is because the center of gravity is usually located near the center of the rib cage just caudal to the intersection of the axis between the cranial and middle thirds of the body.

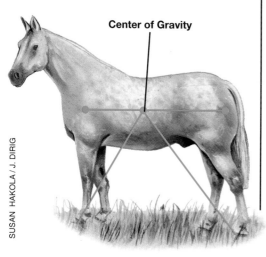

Center of Gravity

The factors of balance and center of gravity gain importance when one views a horse jumping. The long neck provides the jumper with the ability to balance itself when performing. Balance in structure allows a true center of gravity. When imbalances are not ideal, the dynamics of equine locomotion by the musculoskeletal system is greatly affected.

Biomechanics of the Foot

When one examines a newborn's foot from the solar surface, the foot is triangular in shape. An isosceles triangle is formed when measurements are made from the midpoint of the toe caudally to a point on either side terminating at the angle of the wall on the heel of the foot. At birth, the foal's feet begin to grow. They start breaking off or wearing, as Mother Nature intended, when they take their first steps, forming a normal hoof. This is why an abrasive surface is important at this stage of life. Without the bottom of the foot developing normally, the rest of the development of the limbs will be compensated. Foals that are kept in a stall on a soft surface will not wear normally and their feet and limbs will show malformation.

Newborn Foot

When one examines the feet from behind on an even surface, the heels should be the same height on both sides of the foot from the hairline to the ground. Even if the hoof wall contains a wing, the foot should still have a parallel set of lines along the hairline and along the surface coming in contact with the ground (solar surface).

Balanced Foot

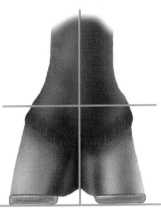

SUSAN HAKOLA

When a force causes the horse to bear an uneven distribution of weight on one side of the foot verses the other, the shifted weight consequently changes the growth of the hoof. The hairline plane and the ground contact plane (solar surface plane) are no longer parallel. The animal responds with an adjustment within the foot to compensate for these uneven forces. Using a medial splint as an example, the animal will bear more weight on the lateral side of the hoof, thus causing a flaring of the medial side of the hoof wall. If this horse is trimmed by completely removing the flared side of the wall instead of the weight bearing side, where there is more growth, one would cause the horse to change the flight of his foot; therefore, the animal would not land evenly on the ground.

Unbalanced Foot

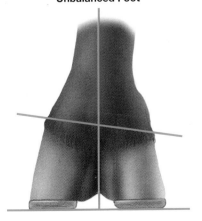

SUSAN HAKOLA

Ideally, the part of the hoof that is the fastest growing should be supported, reestablishing the parallel hairline plane and ground surface contact plane so that the hoof will land evenly on the ground.

The horse will adjust his feet to compensate for any external force on the limb up until three years of age. Proper trimming allows the horse a normal hoof-pastern axis and a normal weight bearing surface, therefore, allowing a normal flight of the horse's foot.

The hoof of the equine is designed to not only bear the weight of the standing horse, but to absorb the shock of concussion. The tubules that are contained within the hoof have a spiral columnar structure that makes them resistant to the forces of compression and flexion.

The interdigitating laminae that allow the attachment of the hoof to the coffin bone redirect the concussive forces that occur. Even though the surface area of the hoof that comes in contact with these concussive forces is only several square inches in area, the laminar attachments expand this area to approximately eight to ten feet of absorbable surface.

Ideal conformation
with parallel sloping
shoulders and
hoof - pastern angle

Many factors influence the reduction in the concussive forces that are absorbed by the equine limb with each step. The angle of the pastern and shoulder, the elasticity of the ligamentous structures, the frog, the lateral cartilages, the digital cushion and

SUSAN HAKOLA / J. DIRIG

the elastic portion of the coronary band all aid in the absorption of concussion. The animal with more slope to the shoulder and pastern deals with less concussive force and can allow more absorption of concussion than the animal with straighter shoulders. The lamina of the foot help diminish the concussive forces and redirect these forces to the hoof and skeleton. The frog acts like a rubber shock absorber. The lateral cartilages are thicker in the forefeet than those found in the hindfeet and are composed of a highly elastic hyaline and fibrous cartilage. The digital cushion is a web-shaped structure that is fibrous and fatty in composition located between the lateral cartilages on the side the deep flexor tendon and the second phalanx dorsally. This cushion absorbs concussive forces and helps protect the bony structures.

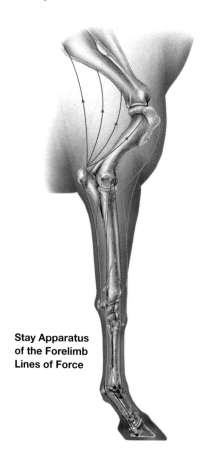

SUSAN HAKOLA / J. DIRIG

**Stay Apparatus
of the Forelimb
Lines of Force**

Stay Apparatus of the Forelimb

The horse has survived for many years using flight as its primary defense. The passive stay apparatus allows the animal to be on its own feet for long periods of time, and even sleep while standing. This ability to stand, without a great deal of muscular effort, allows the horse to be in constant readiness for flight. Basically, the ligaments, tendons, and muscles stabilize the joints into a standing position.

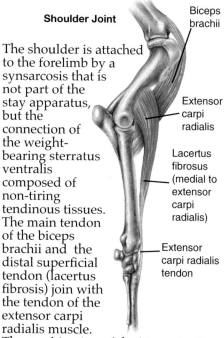

Shoulder Joint

Biceps brachii

Extensor carpi radialis

Lacertus fibrosus (medial to extensor carpi radialis)

Extensor carpi radialis tendon

The shoulder is attached to the forelimb by a synsarcosis that is not part of the stay apparatus, but the connection of the weight-bearing sterratus ventralis composed of non-tiring tendinous tissues. The main tendon of the biceps brachii and the distal superficial tendon (lacertus fibrosis) join with the tendon of the extensor carpi radialis muscle. The combination of the biceps tendon, the lacertus fibrosus and the extensor carpi radialis, from the supraglenoid tubercle to the metacarpal tuberosity, provide a stabilization to the shoulder joint, a cranial force to the elbow, and an extensive force to the carpus.

The elbow joint is stabilized by the long, lateral and medial head of the triceps. It is further stabilized by its own collateral ligaments. The medial ligament is attached above the elbow to the medial epicondyle of the humerus and then divides into two distal portions. The first is a superficial branch terminating on the

Elbow Joint

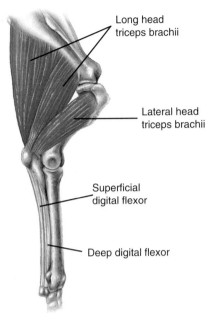

Long head triceps brachii

Lateral head triceps brachii

Superficial digital flexor

Deep digital flexor

medial border of the radius. The second is a deep branch that inserts on the medial tuberosity of the radius. Laterally, the lateral ligament originates on the lateral condyle of the humerus and travels distally to the lateral tuberosity of the radius. Tension is provided by the origin of the carpal and digital flexors from the medial and lateral epicondyles of the humerus.

Carpus Joint

Flexor carpi ulnaris

Extensor carpi radialis

Superior check ligament of the superficial digital flexor

Ulnaris lateralis

Carpus joint

Superficial digital flexor

Inferior check ligament of the deep digital flexor (behind the splint bone)

Deep digital flexor

Stabilization of the carpal joint is provided by several structures. The extensor carpi radialis prevents flexion. The flexor carpi ulnaris and ulnaris lateralis aid in keeping the carpus extended. The check ligaments of the superficial and deep digital flexors both apply a force to the carpus distally. Overextension of the carpus is counteracted by the articular surfaces of the carpal bones.

Fetlock Joint, Palmar View

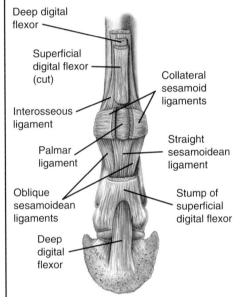

Deep digital flexor

Superficial digital flexor (cut)

Interosseous ligament

Palmar ligament

Oblique sesamoidean ligaments

Deep digital flexor

Collateral sesamoid ligaments

Straight sesamoidean ligament

Stump of superficial digital flexor

SUSAN HAKOLA / J. DIRIG

The fetlock is stabilized by preventing it from overextending. This is accomplished with three structures: the suspensory apparatus which includes the interosseus ligament, the proximal sesamoid bones, and the sesamoidean ligaments. (These include the collateral sesamoid ligaments, the short and cruciate sesamoidean ligaments, the straight sesamoidean ligament and the oblique sesamoidean ligament.) The superficial digital flexor with the superior check ligament and the deep digital flexor with the inferior check ligamentare the other two stabilizing structure groups to the fetlock joint.

With these structures, there are ligaments extending from the proximal end of the large metacarpal bone to the proximal and middle phalanges. The primary structures are reinforced by the superficial and deep digital flexor tendons. The superficial flexor tendon travels from the accessory check ligament on the radius to the proximal and middle phalanx. The deep digital flexor tendon extends from the carpal check ligament to the distal phalanx.

Pastern Joint

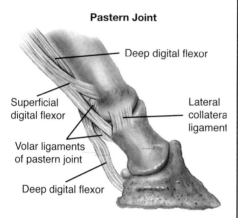

Deep digital flexor

Superficial digital flexor

Lateral collatera ligament

Volar ligaments of pastern joint

Deep digital flexor

Four pastern ligaments prevent overextension of the pastern joint. Additional support is given by the superficial and deep digital tendons and the straight sesamoidean ligament of the suspensory apparatus. The straight distal sesamoidean ligament has cartilagenous attachments to the middle phalanx. Palmar force is also exerted on the pastern joint by the superficial digital flexor tendon.

Coffin Joint

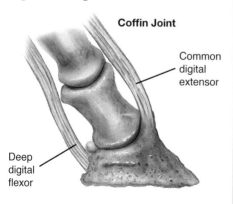

Common digital extensor

Deep digital flexor

The coffin joint is stabilized, to a certain degree, dorsally by the insertion of the common digital

extensor tendon and on the palmar surface by the insertion of the deep digital flexor tendon.

Stay Apparatus of the Hindlimb

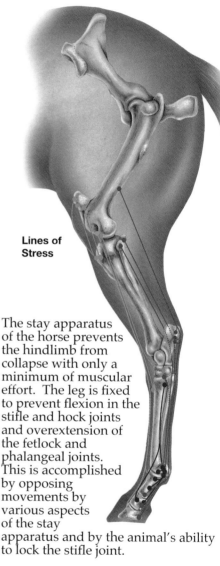

Lines of Stress

The stay apparatus of the horse prevents the hindlimb from collapse with only a minimum of muscular effort. The leg is fixed to prevent flexion in the stifle and hock joints and overextension of the fetlock and phalangeal joints. This is accomplished by opposing movements by various aspects of the stay apparatus and by the animal's ability to lock the stifle joint.

The stifle and hock joints are stabilized by the stay apparatus due to a reciprocal mechanism. The tendinous peroneus tertius muscle and the tendinous superficial digital flexor muscle both cross the joint spaces of the two joints. The peroneus tertius arises from the lateral condyle of the femur, passes cranial to the tibia, and ends by its attachments on the tarsal bones and the proximal end

Reciprocal Mechanism

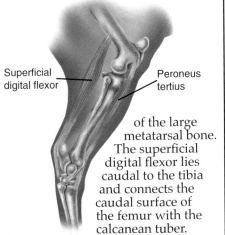

Superficial digital flexor

Peroneus tertius

of the large metatarsal bone. The superficial digital flexor lies caudal to the tibia and connects the caudal surface of the femur with the calcanean tuber. Therefore, if the stifle joint is locked, and the stifle and hock must move in unison, then the hock joint is also rendered incapable of movement.

Anatomy of the Hock, Fetlock, and Pastern Joints, Lateral View

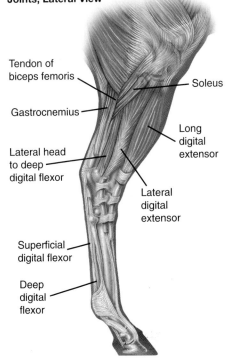

Tendon of biceps femoris

Soleus

Gastrocnemius

Long digital extensor

Lateral head to deep digital flexor

Lateral digital extensor

Superficial digital flexor

Deep digital flexor

Hip Anatomy

Tensor fascia latae

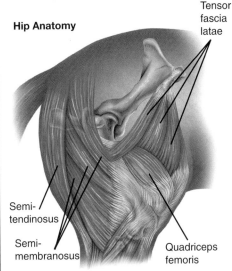

Semi-tendinosus

Semi-membranosus

Quadriceps femoris

The two main differences between the distal hindlimb and the distal forelimb are: 1) The inferior check ligament of the deep digital flexor is much thinner and may be absent. 2) The superficial digital flexor tendon has no accessory ligament, but is instead firmly attached to the calcanean tuber.

When the horse is at rest, one notices that the animal will periodically shift, rest one hind limb, and then shift weight to rest the other. The ability to do this lies in the locking mechanism of the stifle joint. With the ligament and tendinous attachments, the locking of the stifle joint allows the horse to convert the hindlimb into a weight-bearing post. This ability to lock the stifle joint is accomplished by asymmetrical femoral trochlea, the patella and two of the three patellar ligaments.

Locking Mechanism of the Stifle

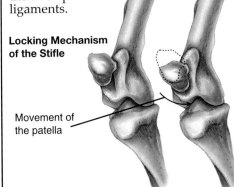

Movement of the patella

SUSAN HAKOLA / J. DIRIG

Stifle Joint

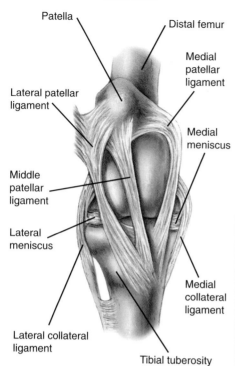

Patella

Distal femur

Medial patellar ligament

Lateral patellar ligament

Medial meniscus

Middle patellar ligament

Lateral meniscus

Medial collateral ligament

Lateral collateral ligament

Tibial tuberosity

SUSAN HAKOLA / J. DIRIG

The medial ridge of the trochlea is larger than the lateral ridge and forms a rounded tubercle. The medial patellar ligament connects to the medial border of the patella, while the intermediate patellar ligament attaches directly to the patellar apex. These two ligaments form from a common origin on the tibial tuberosity, and with the patella, form a loop that is associated with the tubercle on the medial trochlear ridge of the femur. Therefore, when the horse is standing squarely on both hindlimbs, the patella rests on the proximal end of the trochlea and this loop is not coming fully in contact with the tubercle. When the horse

rests one hindleg on the toe of the hoof, the patella in the supporting limb rotates medially, and the medial patellar ligament slides further caudally on the tubercle, fully locking the stifle.

The interosseus ligament that arises proximal to the fetlock and attaches to the proximal sesamoid bones, the distal sesamoidean ligaments (which attach to the plantar surface of the proximal two phalanges) and the superficial and deep flexor tendons all lead to a stabilization of the fetlock and phalangeal joints. These tendons and ligaments are under tension when there is an overextension of the fetlock. They support the joint by preventing it from further overextension.

The limb is further stabilized by the two digital flexor tendons. The superficial digital flexor tendon extends distally from the tuber calcanei to provide some support to the limb plantarly. The deep digital flexor tendon joins with the subtarsal check ligament from the thick plantar part of the tarsal joint capsule as it descends distally.

Overextension of the fetlock and phalangeal joints is accomplished by the stabilization of the digital flexor tendons as they travel to their insertions on the digits, the extensor branches of the suspensory ligaments, and the sesamoidean ligaments. The extensor branches of the suspensory ligament travel from the proximal sesamoid bone to the long digital extensor tendon. The sesamoidean ligaments, especially those located distally, form a brace for the fetlock from their origins on the sesamoid bones to their individual insertions.

℧

The Hoof and the Hoof-Pastern Axis

The hoof is the foundation of the horse. Beware of the mistake that has befallen many when they first examined a horse. Great value is often placed on the appearance of the head. The impression of the head biases the opinion of the remainder of the horse. Countless times, it can be noted that a particular horse has a beautiful head, but terribly conformed feet. If the conformation of the foot is inadequate, then the animal cannot fulfill useful functions.

The size of the feet should be proportional to the size of the horse. Many Quarter horses and Thoroughbreds have feet that are too small to bear the body weight. Therefore, these horses are subject to a greater concussive force within a smaller surface area predisposing the animal to lameness.

The walls should be thick enough to bear the weight of the horse. They should have good growth qualities and be pliable rather than dry. The wall structure in some breeds, such as Saddlebreds and Tennessee Walkers, are allowed to grow abnormally to create the desired action these breeds perform. This also predisposes the animal to lameness conditions such as tendon problems and contracted heels.

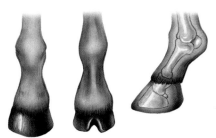

Dorsal View   Palmar View   Lateral View

Ideally the hoof should be **balanced.** The coronary band should be the same

distance from the ground on both the medial and lateral sides of the wall. A transverse line dividing the longitudinal axis of the cannon bone crossed by perpendicular lines at the heel to the ground, should result in two 90 degree angles. The hoof should be smooth and straight and should be proportionate to the size of the animal. The sole and frog should be healthy and present a good contact surface with the ground. The heels should be open and approximately one quarter of the circumference of the whole hoof.

The hoof/pastern axis is a plumb line that theoretically passes through the center of the pastern and the hoof dividing it into equal parts from both the anterior to posterior and lateral to medial views. The normal axis for the front feet should be 45 to 50 degrees and the axis for the hind feet should be 50 to 55 degrees. If there is a deviation to these axes in relation to each other, then many pathological changes may occur within these anatomical structures. When viewed laterally, the dorsal surface of the hoof wall and the slope of the pastern should be parallel lines. If they are not the same, then as the foot hits the ground, a less than ideal utilization of the fetlock shock- absorbing system will result.

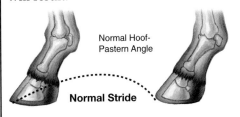

Normal Hoof-Pastern Angle

Normal Stride

SUSAN HAKOLA / J. DIRIG

If the toe is too long and the heel is too low, the foot is referred to as "broken back." This accentuates strain on the deep digital flexor tendons and associated structures. The angle will be less than 45 degrees and will cause a delayed breakover when the animal is in motion. The peak of the arc of flight occurs before the foot reaches the opposite supporting limb. The stride will therefore be longer than that of a normal hoof/pastern axis.

Long Toe-Short Heel Pastern Angle

Long Stride

When the angle of the axis is greater than 50 degrees in the front feet, the heel is high and the toe is short. This axis is referred to as "broken forward." The summit of the flight arch occurs after the foot passes the opposite supporting foot.

Short Toe-Long Heel Pastern Angle

Short Stride

This results in a short stride and a very uncomfortable ride. There is an increased amount of concussive forces that in turn predisposes the animal to the formation of ringbone and arthritis within the corresponding joints.

"Coon-Footed"   **"Club-Footed"**

A "coon-footed" horse has a pastern that slopes back away from the axis of the dorsal surface of the hoof wall. The hoof/pastern axis is broken back at the coronary band. This animal is predisposed to injury to the sesamoid bones and the flexor tendons.

When the foot has an axis of 60 degrees or greater, it is referred to as a "club foot." Terms such as contracted foot or flexural deformity are also used synonymously with the clubfoot syndrome. When this is an inheritable trait, it can be either unilateral or bilateral and is usually confined to the forefeet. Club foot deformities are typically due to a deformity of the deep digital flexor tendon. Sometimes, the suspensory ligament and/or superficial flexor tendon may also be involved. These animals are usually very unsound.

Clubfeet can be categorized into four different grades. They are as follows:

Grade One: merely a mismatching of the feet with the hoof angle of the clubfoot being 5 degrees greater than its opposite.

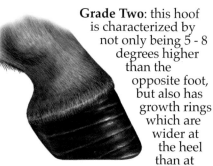

Grade Two: this hoof is characterized by not only being 5 - 8 degrees higher than the opposite foot, but also has growth rings which are wider at the heel than at the toe. If the foot is trimmed to its normal length, the heel will not touch the ground.

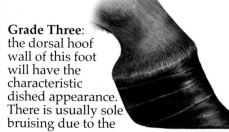

Grade Three: the dorsal hoof wall of this foot will have the characteristic dished appearance. There is usually sole bruising due to the

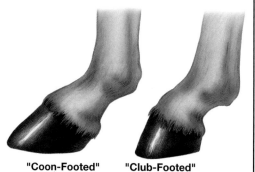

sole having a weight bearing property. Radiographically, there will be lipping along the coffin bone.

Grade Four: the hoof wall of this foot will be greater than 80 degrees. The sole will be a weight bearing structure, and the dorsal hoof wall will have a heavy dished appearance. Radiographics of the distal phalanx will show several degrees of rotation and will be demineralized.

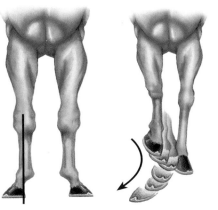

Toe-Out "Winging"-Foot Swings Inward and May Cause Interference During Gait Pattern

"Toed-out" conformation refers to the instances when the plumb line drawn through the center of the foot illustrates the toe deviating outward away from the midline. The wall of the hoof flares on the outside and is upright on the inside. The majority of the weight bearing area is medial. The affected limb interferes with the other limbs during flight, called "winging." This causes tissue trauma and sometimes bony damage can occur.

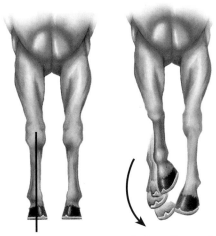

Toe-In "Paddling"-Foot Swings Outward During Gait Pattern

When an animal is referred to as "pigeon toed," the feet will toe in towards the median plane. A plumb line drawn through the center of the hoof illustrates that the toe deviates inward. When in motion, the outside wall of the hoof will bear the majority of the animal's weight. The inside wall will appear to grow faster and paddle. When viewed in motion, the foot will swing outward during the flight path.

Toe- Out
Flight Pattern:
Weight of Foot
on Medial Aspect

Contraction of the heels is always accompanied by contraction of the foot itself. This may be unilaterally or bilaterally. Heel contraction occurs in the front feet more often than the hind feet. The appearance of the foot shows

Toe-In Flight
Pattern:
Weight of
Foot on
Lateral
Aspect.

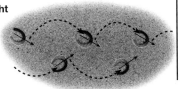

Normal Hoof   Contracted Heel

SUSAN HAKOLA / J. DIRIG

a generalized narrowing, especially around the heel. The frog is usually recessed and atrophied, and the sole generally exhibits an unusual concavity.

Contraction of the foot and heel is usually caused by improper shoeing. It is present in some breeds merely due to how the horses are shod with no frog pressure; i.e.: Tennessee Walkers and American Saddlebreds. Other explanations for this condition may be purely hereditary or as a result of a lameness elsewhere in the limb. Regardless of the cause, this condition usually has a great effect on the animal's ability to perform.

Forelimb Conformation

Examination of the conformation of the forelimbs should occur on a flat, hard surface with the animal bearing weight on all four limbs. The feet, when viewed laterally, should be even or square with the limbs being straight. The knees should face anteriorly and the cannon bone should be located beneath the knee and not deviated laterally or medially. The distance between the feet placed on the ground should equal the distance of the forelimb origins at the chest wall.

The Romans named the horse *"equus"* which, when literally translated, means that it carries itself in balance on all four legs. At rest, however, the horse bears 65% of its weight on the forelimbs. In motion, the weight is more evenly distributed. Ideal conformation of the forelimbs allows for a greater balance and a lesser predisposition for injury to the tissues.

The Shoulders

The model shoulder, when viewed laterally, should be oblique or sloping which provides the animal with a built-in shock absorber. This angle is measured from the point of the withers to the point of the shoulder.

The more angulation that the shoulder has, the longer the stride in motion. If the shoulder is straighter, the stride in motion is shorter, due to a lesser range of motion. If the animal is asked to travel one mile, the animal with the straighter conformed shoulder will have to hit the ground more times than that animal with the more obliquely conformed shoulder. Multiply this factor by the number of miles in a lifetime to realize the amount of stress to the tissues.

The angle of the pastern should match the angle of the shoulder. If the angle of the pastern is straight, as with the shoulder, again the natural shock-absorbing system is compromised. There is more of an increase in the number of times that a horse has to place its feet on the ground to cover a specific distance.

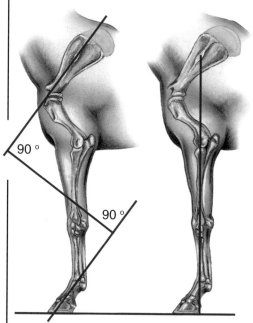

90 °

90 °

Parallel Shoulder-Pastern Angle Ideal Conformation

Ideal General Lateral Profile

General Conformation

Theoretically, from a lateral view, a plumb line should descend from the tuber spinae on the spine of the scapula, to completely bisect the limb through the fetlock and end at a point touching the most posterior aspect of the heel. From the cranial view, a plumb line should travel distally from a point originating at the center of the scapulohumeral joint. It should bisect the limb equally and end at a point on the center of the toe.

With these ideal conformation structures, all of the concussion forces, which result when the foot impacts the ground during exercise, should be distributed evenly throughout the tissues. The resultant stress and strain is; therefore, fully absorbed by the natural shock-absorbing system without creating injuries.

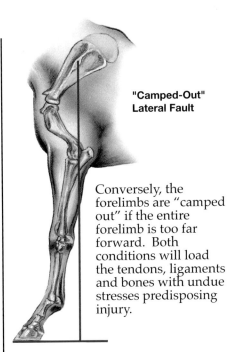

"Camped-Out" Lateral Fault

Conversely, the forelimbs are "camped out" if the entire forelimb is too far forward. Both conditions will load the tendons, ligaments and bones with undue stresses predisposing injury.

Base Narrow Cranial Fault

When viewed cranially, if the plumb line descends distally and does not bisect the limb but ends in a point lateral to the foot, the conformation is referred to as "base narrow." Both of the feet are closer to the median plane. This animal will always bear more weight on the outside of the foot than on the inside. Combine this with feet that are toed-in. The stresses to the outside of the foot when landing are then magnified by a factor of their respective degree of abnormalities. This limb will swing out in motion. The animal is predisposed to strains and stresses to the lateral limb which could result in windpuffs, lateral ringbone, lateral articular damage and bruising of the lateral heel.

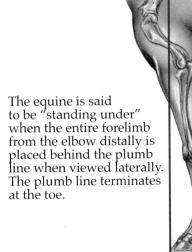

The equine is said to be "standing under" when the entire forelimb from the elbow distally is placed behind the plumb line when viewed laterally. The plumb line terminates at the toe.

"Standing-Under" Lateral Fault

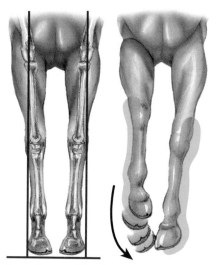

Base Narrow: "Toe-In"   "Paddling"

The animal can be base-narrow and toe-out. This will result in interference with the other limbs. The horse possesses a predisposing tendency to land on the outside wall of the hoof, a motion commonly called "paddling.".

When viewed cranially, if the plumb line descends distally from the middle of the scapulo-humeral joint and terminates medially to the hoof, this animal is referred to as "base wide." Both of the feet are further away from the median plane. This occurs in breeds with narrow chests such as the American saddle-bred. The animal will land on the inside of the hoof causing stress and strain to the medial anatomical structures of the limb. This predisposes the animal to medial windpuffs, medial ringbone and bruising to the medial heel of the foot.

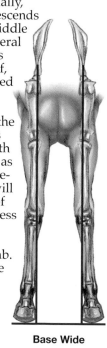

Base Wide

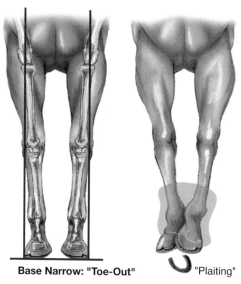

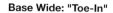

Base Narrow: "Toe-Out"   "Plaiting"

With the feet being closer to the median plane added to a tendency to "wing in," interference fractures or injuries to the fetlock joint can occur. The animal may exhibit a gait called "plaiting" wherein during exercise, the animal places one forefoot directly in front of the other.

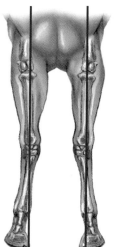

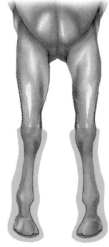

Base Wide: "Toe-In"   Areas of Stress

The animal can "toe-in" and be "base wide," although this fault combination is not nearly as common. The horse can paddle to the outside or wing to the inside, including the entire spectrum between, depending on any other abnormalities of the limb.

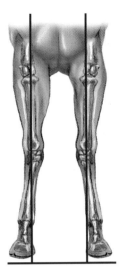

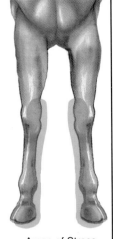

Base Wide: "Toe-Out"   Areas of Stress

"Base wide" conformation, combined with the feet being "toed-out," is a common finding. The animal lands on the inside of the foot and breaks over on the inside toe. This predisposes the horse to stress on the medial collateral ligaments within the joints, medial ringbone, medial sidebone, and stress to the medial splint bone from this conformation fault.

Conformation of the Knee

Conformation problems concerning the knee can result in a range of disorders from merely a strain to the joint capsule, to stained ligaments, arthritis, chip and slab fractures. These conformational defects are seen from observation of the knees in relationship to the plumb lines descending the leg, both cranially and laterally.

The least serious of the conformation faults of the carpus is the forward deviation, from a lateral viewpoint, of the carpus or "over at the knees." The joint normally flexes in this direction; therefore, this fault is more acceptable than the other conformation faults of the carpus. This dorsal deviation will result in strain to the superficial flexor tendon and suspensory ligament and will have a resultant stress on the sesamoid bones.

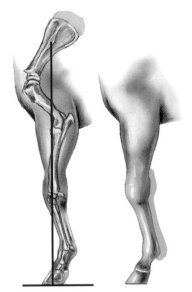

"Over at the Knee"   Stress Area

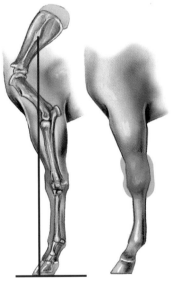

"Calf Knee"   Stress Area

The carpus does not flex backward; therefore, the palmar deviation to the carpus or "calf knees" is a serious fault. This conformation fault results in stress and strain to the carpal and radial check ligaments, the proximal, middle and distal accessory carpal ligaments, and increased compression forces on all of the carpal bones. Chip fractures are commonly found with this fault.

SUSAN HAKOLA / J. DIRIG

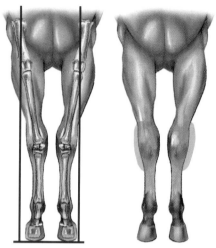

"Knock Knees"   Stress Areas

When the carpus is deviated medially, the horse is referred to as having "knock knees" or "knee narrow" conformation. This fault usually results from a growth plate abnormality. The resultant stresses and strains from this fault cause strain to the medial collateral ligaments of the carpus and more concussion to the lateral surfaces of the carpal bones.

Increased stresses and strains are placed on the lateral surfaces of the limb with more concussive forces focused on the medial carpal bones.

Metacarpal Conformation

The term "bench knees" refers to a fault within the carpus but in reality, it is one in which the metacarpal or cannon bone is offset to the carpus laterally. The greatest predisposition here is the stress to the medial splint bone. Increased stress occurs since it has a full articulation with the carpus; whereas, the lateral splint bone merely carries an oblique articulation. This ensuing stress to the medial splint bone causes strain to the corresponding medial interosseous ligament.

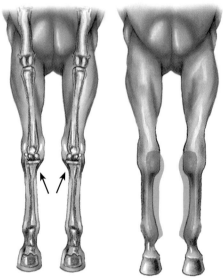

Bench Knees Lateral   Stress Areas
Placement of Metacarpal

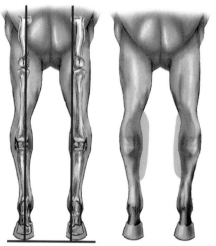

"Bow Leg"   Stress Areas

A lateral deviation of the carpal joints usually accompanies an animal that is base narrow and toed-in. The horse is referred to as "bow-legged."

Conformation of the Pastern

Conformation faults of the pastern fall into three categories: the short upright pastern, the long upright pastern, and the long sloping pastern. Ideally, the angle and length of the pastern will prevent the ankle from being injured by preventing the

SUSAN HAKOLA / J. DIRIG

ankle from striking the ground. At the same time, the pastern length and angle will provide leverage to act as a shock absorber to the ankle joint, the knee, and the rest of the horse's body.

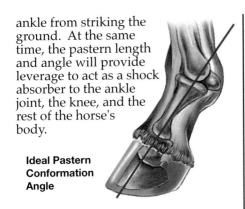

Ideal Pastern Conformation Angle

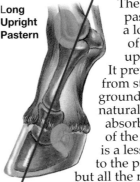

Long Upright Pastern

The long upright pastern is merely a longer version of the short upright pastern. It prevents the ankle from striking the ground, but lacks the natural shock absorbing capability of the norm. There is a lesser trauma to the pastern joint, but all the rest of the concussive force type injuries, osslets and navicular syndrome, can be present with this fault.

Long Sloping Pastern

A long sloping pastern does not prohibit the ankle from striking the ground. The long length also predisposes the horse to strain within the flexor tendons and the suspensory ligament. The sesamoid bones will readily become inflamed and will be more inclined to fractures.

Short Upright Pastern

The short upright pastern prevents injury caused by the ankle striking the ground, but does little to act as a shock absorber. The resultant forces from the concussion of the hoof hitting the ground are brought to bear on the fetlock joint, the proximal inter-phalangeal joint, and the navicular bone. Predisposing lameness problems of arthritis within these joints, navicular syndrome, and osselets can easily be visualized. Animals with short upright pasterns usually have accompanying straight shoulders.

Hindlimb Conformation

The hindquarters are what provides the power to the horse's movement. The forelimbs are not attached to the spinal column directly, but are held in place by muscles and tendons; whereas, the hindquarters are directly attached to the pelvis. With relationship to the center of gravity of the horse, the hindquarters only have to bear 35% of the body weight. Therefore, they do not sustain the same amount of concussive forces as that of the forelimbs.

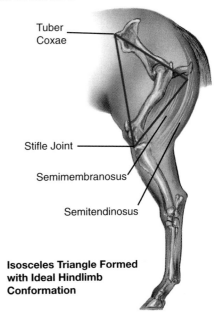

Tuber Coxae

Stifle Joint

Semimembranosus

Semitendinosus

SUSAN HAKOLA / J. DIRIG

Isosceles Triangle Formed with Ideal Hindlimb Conformation

The reasoning behind this is purely biomechanical, because the animal does not push forward off the hindquarters in a simple movement. The tendons are tensed to start the hoof pressing the earth. The force is then transmitted upward through the bony column of the pastern, fetlock, hock, and finally the stifle. The muscling of the hindquarters contracts with force originating over the top line of the hindquarter. This balanced chain of events is what moves the animal forward. If there is any variation in this triangle, there is a lesser degree of balance and a resultant loss of movement.

The stifle is the origin for most of the biomechanical energy involving motion. This area of muscle should be well developed both laterally and medially. The hock joint acts as a free flowing lever of the hind limb and aids in the transferring of the energy from the hindquarter muscling to the hoof. The hock withstands a tremendous amount of concussive force and stress from all of the athletic events.

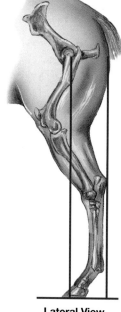

Laterally, ideal conformation of the hindquarters can be visualized by a plumbline descending distally from the tip of the tuber ischii, contacting the point of the hock, flowing parallel and plantar to the metatarsal and terminating just a few inches behind the heel.

Lateral View

Caudal View

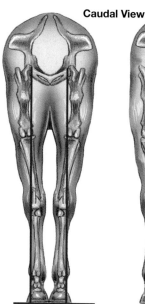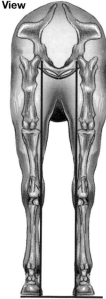

Base Narrow   **Base Wide**

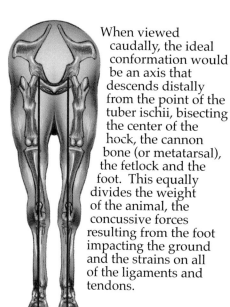

When viewed caudally, the ideal conformation would be an axis that descends distally from the point of the tuber ischii, bisecting the center of the hock, the cannon bone (or metatarsal), the fetlock and the foot. This equally divides the weight of the animal, the concussive forces resulting from the foot impacting the ground and the strains on all of the ligaments and tendons.

Caudal View

When the animal is viewed caudally, the conformation faults of base narrow and base wide, and the angulation of the hocks will be noted. The base narrow conformation of the hindlimb is similar to that of the forelimb. Both hind feet are closer to the median plane. The plumb line descends laterally to the hoof. As with the

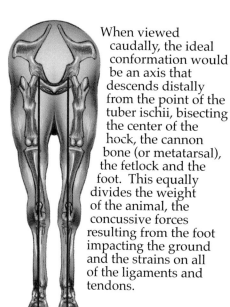

SUSAN HAKOLA / J. DIRIG

forelimb, interference with the other limbs during motion will occur.

"Cow-Hocked"

When the conformational fault of being base wide occurs with the hindquarter, it is usually associated with the fault of being "cow hocked." Both hind feet are spaced further away from the median plane than the bisecting descending plumb line from the hip.

A medial deviation of the hock joint is also referred to as the animal being "cow hocked." In this case, the limb is either normal or base narrow to the hock and then base wide distal to the hock joint when viewed caudally. This predisposes the animal to excessive strain on the medial surfaces of the hock joint, resulting in bone spavin.

When viewed laterally, four conformational faults involving the entire hind limb can be visualized.

These faults are: "straight behind" or "post legged," "camped out behind," "standing under," and "sickled hocked." They are all self-explanatory in nomenclature.

The "post legged" conformation fault is derived from a lack of angle within the stifle joint. The hock joint is straight in anatomical structure. When visualized, the animal appears as a rump stuck on a fence post. This fault predisposes the animal to an upward fixation of the patella as well as a myriad of changes within the hock joint such as bone and bog spavin.

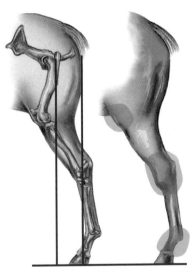

"Camped-Out Behind"   Areas of Stress

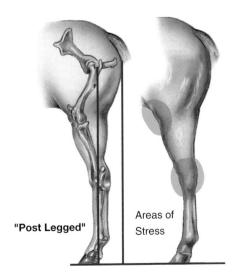

"Post Legged"   Areas of Stress

When the animal is shod at an angle to create an upright pastern angle, or if the pasterns are upright from a genetic conformational fault, the horse will appear "camped out behind." The plumb line descending from the hip will terminate on the toe or in front of the toe of the hind foot. This animal will not only create strain and stress on all the articular surfaces, but will also lack the biomechanical ability to efficiently move forward.

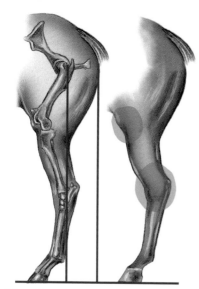

"Standing Under"   Areas of Stress

Horsemen refer to an animal as "curby behind" when there is an excessive angulation of the hock joint or "sickle hocks." Laterally, the limb appears to deviate under the horse from the hock down. As indicated by the name from the horsemen, this animal is predisposed to a strain of the plantar ligament which is referred to as a curb.

Converse to the conformational fault of being "camped out" is the conformational fault of "standing under." The plumb line here would descend and terminate far behind the heel of the foot. This is usually seen associated with an excessive angulation of the hocks.

Conclusions

Good conformation is one of the key building blocks in allowing the equine the ability to perform its' tasks with greatest efficiency. The usefulness and longevity is based on the horse's individual ability to perform. Without good conformation, the horse is handicapped in its ability to perform at its maximum potential or for a long period of time.

On an anecdotal note, an examination was made of a third level dressage horse that was nine years old. This animal exhibited at least six major conformational faults. When the new owners were questioned concerning the wisdom of this purchase, they merely replied: " We didn't want a pre-purchase exam because we knew you would find fault with him and we know he will perform for us." That animal competed successfully for three years at that level with virtually no lameness problems. The lesson that this horse bestowed was that there are no plumb lines for disposition and heart. There are no illustrations for the comparison of the heart of one horse to the next. When one speaks of the horse, without a good disposition and heart, even the most ideal conformation will be in wastage.
Ʊ

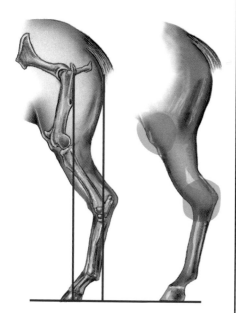

"Sickle-Hocked"   Areas of Stress

The thoracic limb can be divided into four separate sections: the shoulder, which includes the shoulder girdle and scapulohumeral joint, the arm, the forearm, and the manus. There is not any bony attachment of the forearm to the axial skeleton as there is with the hindlimb. This attachment is completed with muscular and ligamentous structures connecting the forelimb to the trunk.

thickened middle portion of the spine, serves as a reference point for the descending plumb lines concerning conformation evaluation. The cartilaginous border is incorporated into the withers.

Left Shoulder Bony Anatomy

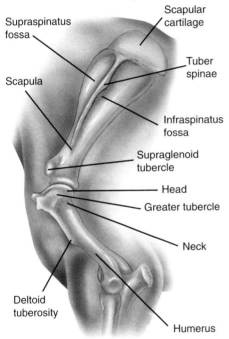

- Suprapinatus fossa
- Scapular cartilage
- Tuber spinae
- Scapula
- Infraspinatus fossa
- Supraglenoid tubercle
- Head
- Greater tubercle
- Neck
- Deltoid tuberosity
- Humerus

**Left Scapula
Lateral View**

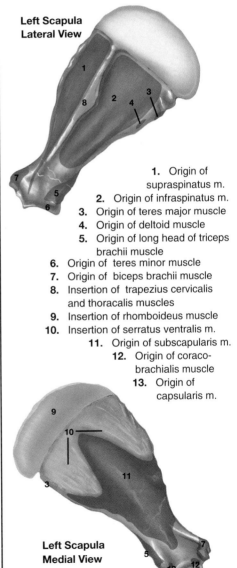

1. Origin of suprapinatus m.
2. Origin of infraspinatus m.
3. Origin of teres major muscle
4. Origin of deltoid muscle
5. Origin of long head of triceps brachii muscle
6. Origin of teres minor muscle
7. Origin of biceps brachii muscle
8. Insertion of trapezius cervicalis and thoracalis muscles
9. Insertion of rhomboideus muscle
10. Insertion of serratus ventralis m.
11. Origin of subscapularis m.
12. Origin of coraco-brachialis muscle
13. Origin of capsularis m.

**Left Scapula
Medial View**

SUSAN HAKOLA / J. DIRIG

The Bony Anatomy of the Shoulder

The scapula is a flat bone that is unique because of its cartilaginous dorsal border, lateral palpable spine and distal scapulohumeral articulation. The orientation of the spine of the scapula is of interest to horsemen. A more sloping shoulder is the conformation preference in saddle horses. The tuber spinae, the

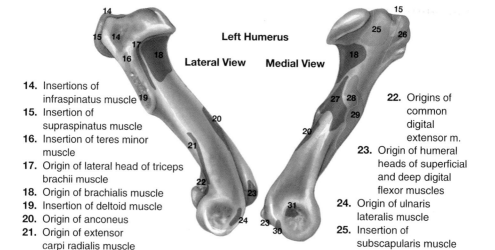

Left Humerus

Lateral View   **Medial View**

14. Insertions of infraspinatus muscle
15. Insertion of supraspinatus muscle
16. Insertion of teres minor muscle
17. Origin of lateral head of triceps brachii muscle
18. Origin of brachialis muscle
19. Insertion of deltoid muscle
20. Origin of anconeus
21. Origin of extensor carpi radialis muscle

22. Origins of common digital extensor m.
23. Origin of humeral heads of superficial and deep digital flexor muscles
24. Origin of ulnaris lateralis muscle
25. Insertion of subscapularis muscle

SUSAN HAKOLA / J. DIRIG

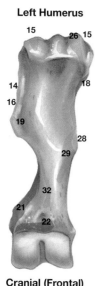

Left Humerus

14. Insertions of infraspinatus muscle
15. Insertion of supraspinatus muscle
16. Insertion of teres minor muscle
17. Origin of lateral head of triceps brachii m.
18. Origin of brachialis muscle
19. Insertion of deltoid muscle
20. Origin of anconeus
21. Origin of extensor carpi radialis muscle
22. Origins of common digital extensor muscle
23. Origin of humeral heads of superficial and deep digital flexor muscles
24. Origin of ulnaris lateralis muscle
25. Insertion of subscapularis muscle
26. Insertion of caudal deep pectoral muscle
27. Origin of medial head of triceps brachii m.
28. Insertion of latissimus dorsi and teres major muscle tendon
29. Insertion of coracobrachialis muscle
30. Origin of flexor carpi ulnaris muscle
31. Origin of flexor carpi radialis muscle
32. Insertion of capsularis muscle

Cranial (Frontal) View

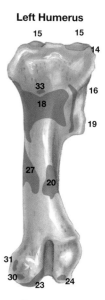

Left Humerus

Caudal View

The Muscles of the Shoulder Girdle

The shoulder girdle is composed of muscle aponeuroses and ligamentous attachments. There are similarities between this attachment and that of other species with the differences being those that allow maximum range of motion for the locomotor speed of the equine.

The *trapezius* muscle covers eight underlying muscles and originates from an aponeurosis along the dorsal midline, close to the poll, and inserts along the scapular spine. There is a cervical and thoracic division to this muscle, depending on its anatomical location. Each division may act together to elevate the shoulder or independently to cause a cranial or caudal motion.

Superficial Muscle Layer of the Shoulder, Right Lateral View

Rhomboideus

Splenius

Omotransversarius

Trapezius cervicalis

Trapezius thoracis

Latissimus dorsi

Serratus ventralis cervicis

Subclavius (anterior deep pectoral)

Brachiocephalicus

Deltoideus

Pectoralis descendens (Anterior superficial pectoral)

Brachialis

Serratus thoracis

Extensor carpi radialis

Long head triceps brachii

Common digital extensor

Pectoralis ascendens (Posterior superficial pectoral)

Lateral head triceps brachii

SUSAN HAKOLA / J. DIRIG

The *rhomboideus* muscle lies just beneath the trapezius with an origin on the nuchal and supraspinous ligaments and an insertion on the medial side of the scapular cartilage. This muscle not only has the function of elevation of the scapula in a dorso-cranial direction, but when the animal is at rest, the cervical portion of the rhomboideus aids in the elevation of the neck.

The widest muscle of the shoulder girdle is the *latissimus dorsi* which originates from the supraspinous ligament and the thoracolumbar fascia to insert upon the teres tuberosity of the humerus. This muscle is the antagonist of the brachiocephalicus muscle in that it retracts the limb. After the limb is extended and advanced, the latissimus dorsi pulls the trunk onto this limb. The insertion upon the teres tuberosity is shared with the tendon of the teres major muscle.

The substantial portion of the synsarcosis of the shoulder to the trunk, from superficial to deep, are the *brachiocephalicus*, the

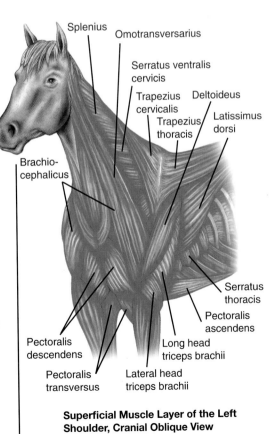

Splenius

Omotransversarius

Serratus ventralis cervicis

Trapezius cervicalis

Deltoideus

Trapezius thoracis

Latissimus dorsi

Brachio-cephalicus

Serratus thoracis

Pectoralis ascendens

Pectoralis descendens

Long head triceps brachii

Pectoralis transversus

Lateral head triceps brachii

Superficial Muscle Layer of the Left Shoulder, Cranial Oblique View

omotransversarius, the *anterior* and *posterior superficial pectorals*, the *anterior* and *posterior deep pectoral muscles* and the *serratus ventralis muscle*.

Extending from the mastoid region of the skull and traversing down the side of the neck to the arm is the *brachiocephalicus* muscle. It originates upon the mastoid process of the temporal bone, the wing of the atlas and the transverse processes of the second, third and fourth cervical vertebrae to insert on the deltoid tuberosity and crest of the humerus. The brachiocephalicus has the action of drawing the limb forward when the head and neck are fixed.

Superficial Muscles of the Shoulder Girdle, Ventral View

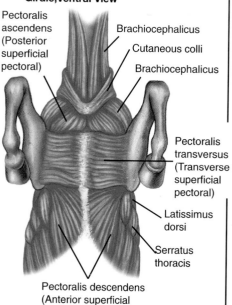

Pectoralis ascendens (Posterior superficial pectoral)

Brachiocephalicus

Cutaneous colli

Brachiocephalicus

Pectoralis transversus (Transverse superficial pectoral)

Latissimus dorsi

Serratus thoracis

Pectoralis descendens (Anterior superficial pectoral)

SUSAN HAKOLA / J. DIRIG

As it trasverses from the point of the shoulder, dorsal to the brachio-cephalicus, to the atlas and first few cervical vertebrae dorsal to the brachiocephalicus, the *omotransversarius* combines with the trapezius dorsally and functions to help elevate the scapula and move the limb forward. The origin of the *omotransversarius* is the wing of the atlas and the transverse processes of the second, third, and fourth

cervical vertebrae. The insertion is the humeral crest and fascia of the shoulder and arm.

All four pectoral muscles function to adduct the limb. There is a superficial layer of two muscles, the *pectoralis descendens* and the *pectoralis transversus*, and a deep layer of two muscles, the *pectoralis profundus* and the *subclavius*, which all occupy the space between the chest wall and the shoulder. All four originate on different areas of the sternum.

The pectoralis descendens originates upon the cariniform cartilage of the sternum and inserts on the deltoid tuberosity and the crest of the humerus along with the brachiocephalicus. The other superficial pectoral muscle that lies posteriorly is the pectoralis transversus, which aids in adduction of the limb and tenses the fascia of the forearm. It has an origin on the ventral edge of the sternum and it inserts on the fascia of the proximal third of the forearm.

The largest of the four pectoralis muscles is the deep pectoralis profundus. This muscle originates on the caudal aspect of the sternum and the abdominal floor. It inserts on the cranial parts of the lesser and greater tubercles of the humerus and the tendon of the coracobrachialis muscle.

The anterior portion of the deep pectoral muscles is the subclavius. It originates on the cranial part of the sternum and inserts in an aponeurosis covering the supraspinatus at the dorsal end. The pectoral muscles all adduct the limb but the superficial pectorals will also tense the antebrachial fascia. The deep pectorals, when the limb is advanced, will also aid in the movement of the trunk cranially.

The *serratus ventralis* consists of a cervical and thoracic portion. The cervical portion, the *serratus cervicus* originates on the transverse process of the last four or five cervical vertebrae and inserts on the costal surface of the scapula. The thoracic portion, the *serratus thoracis,* has an origin on the lateral surfaces of the first eight or nine ribs and inserts on the posterior triangular area of the costal surface of the scapula. Both portions act antagonistically in that the cervical portion draws the base of the scapula towards the neck, while the thoracic portion has the opposite effect. Both of these muscle bundles facilitate the backward and forward movement of the forelimb.

The dorsoscapular ligament gives origin to the *rhomboideus thoracis* muscle dorsally, the *splenius* muscle cranially, and deep to these, the *semispinalis capitis.* It affords attachment of the limb to the trunk from thickened fascia of the third, fourth, and fifth thoracic spines. After giving origin to these muscles, the dorsoscapular ligament thins to form numerous lamellae which intersect the scapular part of the serratus ventralis and attaches to the scapula.

Practical Applications of the Shoulder Girdle Muscles

The *trapezius* muscle is not only responsible for cranial and caudal motion, but has other important functions. It aids in applying force to the scapulohumeral joint by drawing the scapula dorsally and caudally. If there is a problem with this muscle, the animal will exhibit a slight dip in the neck when viewed laterally. The horse will be unable to elevate the shoulder and forearm and will lack coordination in the forward motion.

Problems with the *rhomboideus* will not only affect the coordination of the shoulder but will not allow the animal to elevate the neck. When this muscle is stiff or sore, the animal will be reluctant to "set" its' head. In the equine athlete, the neck will not be extended to allow the head to be positioned for the maximum air intake during maximum exertion.

When the *latissimus dorsi* muscle is tight or sore, the animal will ride as if it were imitating a steel girder. The animal will turn very stiffly when asked to circle. This muscle provides support for the dorsal portion of the thorax, retracts the forelimb, and draws the truck or body forward when the limb is fixed and aids in flexion of the scapulohumeral joint.

The *brachiocephalicus* aids in drawing the limb forward, facilitates the extension of the scapulohumeral joint and elevates the shoulder. Problems, such as soreness in this muscle bundle, result in a tightness within the shoulder and an instability of the scapulohumeral joint.

The *superficial* and *deep pectorals* are both adductors of the forelimb. When these muscles are stiff or sore the animal exhibits a shortened stride with the forelimbs. A horse that is reluctant to girthing up may be exhibiting the initial clinical signs of a problem with these muscle groups.

Both the cervical and thoracic portions of the *serratus ventralis* muscle act as a "sling" for the trunk. Stiffness in the forearm may indicate a soreness within this muscle. If the animal is reluctant to turn or circle in either direction, there may be a problem within the serratus. When the animal is in motion, the *serratus ventralis* acts antagonistically between its cervical and thoracic portions to allow a backward and forward movement of the forelimb.

Muscles That Function as Ligaments for the Scapulohumeral Joint

There is a group of muscles that originate on the scapula and insert on the humerus. They can be divided into a lateral and medial group of four. The lateral and medial groups are antagonistic in that the lateral group are all abductors for the arm with the medial group being adductors.

Laterally, the *deltoid* muscle originates along the posterior border and spine of the scapula as well as the aponeurosis which covers the infraspinatus. Its insertion is along the deltoid tuberosity and the brachial fascia. The deltoid flexes the shoulder joint and abducts the arm.

**Deep Muscle Layer
Right Shoulder,
Lateral View**

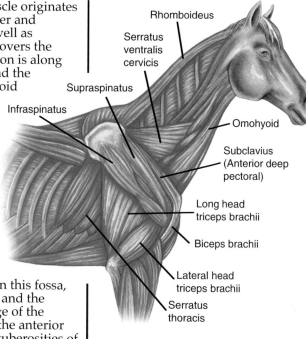

Rhomboideus

Serratus ventralis cervicis

Supraspinatus

Infraspinatus

Omohyoid

Subclavius (Anterior deep pectoral)

Long head triceps brachii

Biceps brachii

Lateral head triceps brachii

Serratus thoracis

Occupying the supraspinous fossa on the scapula is the *supraspinatus* muscle. This muscle originates on this fossa, the spine of the scapula, and the lower part of the cartilage of the scapula. Its insertion is the anterior portion of the proximal tuberosities of the humerus. The primary function of the supraspinatus is to aid in extension of the shoulder and with its two attaching tendons, acts as a ligament to provide stabilization to the scapulohumeral joint.

Located in the infraspinous fossa is another of the lateral muscle group, the *infraspinatus*. This muscle originates in the infraspinous fossa and the scapular cartilage and inserts on the lateral tuberosity of the humerus. With this location, it acts as a lateral ligament to the scapulohumeral joint in addition to abducting the limb and allowing outward rotation.

The smallest member of the lateral group is the *teres minor*. It originates in three anatomical locations: 1.) the most distal and posterior portion of the infraspinous fossa; 2.) the posterior border of the scapula; 3.) on the rim of the glenoid cavity. It inserts on the deltoid tuberosity. In action, the teres minor aids in the flexion of the shoulder joint, abduction of the arm and outward rotation of the limb.

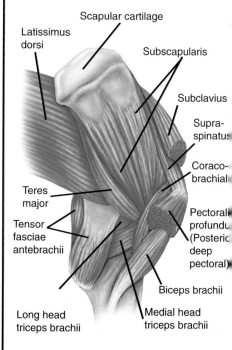

Scapular cartilage

Latissimus dorsi

Subscapularis

Subclavius

Supra-spinatus

Coraco-brachial

Teres major

Pectorali profundu (Posterio deep pectoral)

Tensor fasciae antebrachii

Biceps brachii

Long head triceps brachii

Medial head triceps brachii

**Medial View Left Shoulder
Deep Muscle Layer**

Medially, the *subscapularis* occupies the subscapular fossa, which is its point of origin. It inserts on the medial tuberosity of the humerus. The subscapularis functions to stabilize the scapulo-humeral joint and adducts the arm.

The *teres major* arises from the caudal aspect of the scapula and inserts, along with the latissimus dorsi, on the teres tuberosity of the humerus. It functions to flex the shoulder joint and adduct the humerus.

Arising from the coracoid process of the scapula is the *coracobrachialis* muscle. It inserts on both the teres tuberosity of the humerus and the proximal portion of the shaft of the humerus. This provides some stabilization of the joint and, in a small degree, aids in the adduction of the humerus and flexion of the shoulder.

The *capsularis* muscle is of little consequence and lies on the flexion surface of the capsule of the shoulder joint. It originates on the scapula on the rim of the glenoid cavity and inserts on the posterior surface of the shaft of the humerus. This muscle plays a small part in joint stabilization and adduction.

Neurological Supply to the Shoulder

The brachial plexus is formed by the ventral branches of the sixth cervical vertebra through the second thoracic vertebrae. The axillary nerve arises from the plexus and traverses on the medial surface of the subscapularis muscle to innervate the caudal portion of the subscapularis, the teres major, the deltoideus and the teres minor. The axillary nerve ends by terminating into the cranial cutaneous antebrachial nerve.

Also arising from the brachial plexus are the subscapular, the suprascapular, and the thoracodorsal nerves. The subscapular innervates the subscapularis muscle, whereas the suprascapular nerve supplies both the supraspinatus and infraspinatus muscles. The thoracodorsal nerve innervates the latissimus dorsi muscle.

The brachial plexus also gives rise to the median, ulnar, and radial nerves. The radial and ulnar nerves descend distally, medial to the subscapular artery and lateral to the external thoracic vein. A small branch of the radial nerve supplies the tensor fasciae antebrachii muscle before the main branch descends between the teres major and the triceps brachii. The largest branch arising from the brachial plexus is the median nerve which also descends distally forming a loop around the axillary artery with the musculocutaneous nerve before plunging distally.

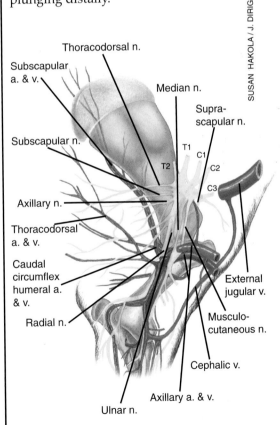

SUSAN HAKOLA / J. DIRIG

Thoracodorsal n.

Subscapular a. & v.

Median n.

Supra-scapular n.

Subscapular n.

T1
C1
T2
C2
C3

Axillary n.

Thoracodorsal a. & v.

Caudal circumflex humeral a. & v.

External jugular v.

Radial n.

Musculo-cutaneous n.

Cephalic v.

Axillary a. & v.

Ulnar n.

Vascular Supply to the Shoulder

The subclavian artery, after dividing the deltoid branch of the superficial cervical artery, becomes the axillary artery. This axillary artery gives origin to the suprascapular, subscapular, thoracodorsal, and the cranial and caudal circumflex humeral arteries. After the subscapular artery arises from the axillary, it is termed the brachial artery as it descends distally. The suprascapular artery supplies the supraspinatus and the lateral scapular muscles. The subscapular artery supplies the caudal border muscles, including the subscapularis, teres major and minor, the deltoideus and the infraspinatus. The latissimus dorsi is supplied by the thoracodorsal artery. The cranial and caudal circumflex humeral vessels supply the pectorals, the coracobrachialis, and the capsularis muscles.

All of the arteries have accompaning venous drainage of like nomenclature, except the cephalic vein, which arises from the external jugular vein. This cephalic vein facilitates drainage from the median, median cubital and accessory cephalic veins.

Anatomy of the Scapulohumeral Joint

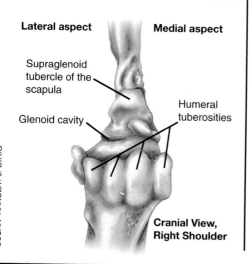

Lateral aspect   Medial aspect

Supraglenoid tubercle of the scapula

Glenoid cavity

Humeral tuberosities

SUSAN HAKOLA / J. DIRIG

Cranial View, Right Shoulder

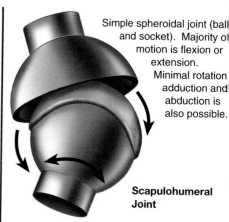

Simple spheroidal joint (ball and socket). Majority of motion is flexion or extension. Minimal rotation adduction and abduction is also possible.

Scapulohumeral Joint

The articular surfaces of the glenoid cavity found on the scapula and the head of the humerus form the scapulohumeral joint. The articular surface of the humerus is approximately twice the area as that of the articular surface of the scapula. Both of the surfaces of the scapula and humerus are spherical and curved in such a way that they articularly oppose each other.

This is a simple spheroidal joint that has extension and flexion as its major movements. The caudal angle of the joint, while in the standing postion, is 120 - 130 degrees and can be increased to 145 degrees upon extension and decreased to 80 degrees in flexion. In reality, it functions closer to a hinge joint with its motions occurring along the sagittal plane.

Numerous muscles attach around the joint space and act as ligaments to provide stabilization to the joint. This joint is unique in that these muscles and their tendinous attachments provide the majority of the stability to the joint instead of ligaments. In addition, the large head of the humerus also guards against dislocation. Laterally, the *supra-spinatus, infraspinatus* and *teres minor* muscles provide stability. On the medial surface, the *subscapularis* muscle offers support. Cranially, the *biceps brachii* and *supraspinatus* muscles allow flexibility yet brace the joint. The *triceps brachii* muscle stabilizes the joint caudally.

The fibrous joint capsule is unique in this anatomical area in that it attaches 1-2 cm. distant from the joint margins to allow the scapula and humerus to be drawn apart 2-3 cm. Cranially, this fibrous joint capsule is reinforced by two ligaments that travel from the supraglenoid tubercle to the tuberosities of the humerus. On the distal and caudal portion of the joint capsule, fibers from the *brachialis* are attached to act as a tensor to the capsule. In some instances, the joint cavity itself communicates with the bicipital bursa.

∪

**Scapulohumeral Joint,
Lateral View, Right Shoulder**

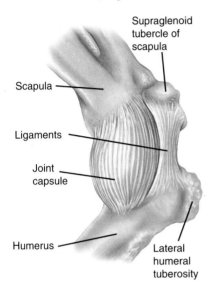

Supraglenoid
tubercle of
scapula

Scapula

Ligaments

Joint
capsule

Humerus

Lateral
humeral
tuberosity

**Scapulohumeral Joint,
Medial View, Right Shoulder**

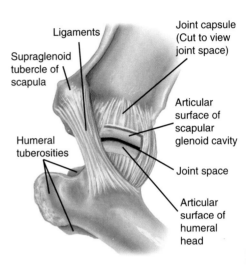

Ligaments

Supraglenoid
tubercle of
scapula

Humeral
tuberosities

Joint capsule
(Cut to view
joint space)

Articular
surface of
scapular
glenoid cavity

Joint space

Articular
surface of
humeral
head

The Upper Arm Bone and Muscular Anatomy

A single long bone, the humerus, and its associated structures, constitutes this anatomical area. It articulates with the scapula at the scapulohumeral joint and descends distally to the elbow at a 55 degree angle to the horizontal plane where it articulates with the radius and ulna.

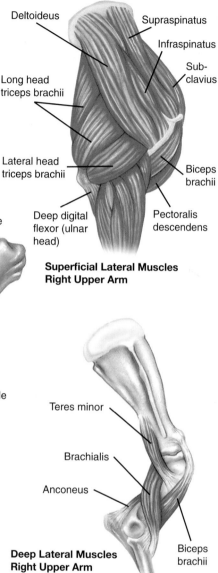

Deltoideus
Supraspinatus
Infraspinatus
Sub-clavius
Long head triceps brachii
Lateral head triceps brachii
Biceps brachii
Deep digital flexor (ulnar head)
Pectoralis descendens

Superficial Lateral Muscles Right Upper Arm

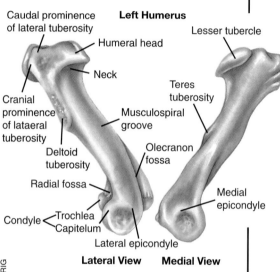

Left Humerus

Caudal prominence of lateral tuberosity
Lesser tubercle
Humeral head
Neck
Teres tuberosity
Cranial prominence of lataeral tuberosity
Musculospiral groove
Deltoid tuberosity
Olecranon fossa
Radial fossa
Medial epicondyle
Condyle — Trochlea Capitelum
Lateral epicondyle

Lateral View   Medial View

SUSAN HAKOLA / J. DIRIG

Teres minor

Brachialis

Anconeus

Biceps brachii

Deep Lateral Muscles Right Upper Arm

There are five muscles that are associated with the arm. The flexor group consists of two muscles, the *biceps brachii* and the *brachialis*. The extensors include the three heads of the *triceps brachii*, the *tensor fasciae antebrachii* and the *anconeus*.

The *biceps brachii* can be palpated on the cranial surface of the humerus after originating on the supraglenoid tubercle of the scapula. The main insertion is on the radial tuberosity, but part of the tendon forms the medial ligament of the elbow. A section also merges with the epimysium of the extensor carpi radialis. The main action of the biceps brachii muscle is to flex the elbow joint and fix the shoulder and elbow while standing.

The only function of the *brachialis* muscle is to flex the elbow. It lies laterally within the spiral groove of the humerus originating from the caudalproximal surface of the humerus and inserting on craniomedial portion of the proximal radius.

The most important muscle of the extensor group is the *triceps brachii*. This muscle fills most of the angle found between the posterior border of the scapula and the humerus. It is easily recognized as having three heads. The long head originates along the posterior border of the scapula and inserts on the lateral and posterior portion of the olecranon. The lateral head arises from the deltoid tuberosity of the humerus and inserts upon the lateral surface of the olecranon. The medial head originates on the medial shaft of the humerus and inserts upon the medial and anterior part of the olecranon.

originates from the distal third of the posterior surface of the humerus and inserts on the lateral surface of the olecranon. It functions to raise the capsule of the joint thus preventing the capsule from being pinched during extension.

Nerves, Arteries and Veins of the Right Upper Arm

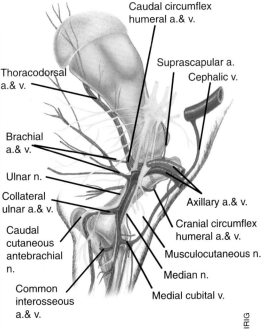

Caudal circumflex humeral a.& v.

Suprascapular a.
Cephalic v.

Thoracodorsal a.& v.

Brachial a.& v.

Ulnar n.

Collateral ulnar a.& v.

Axillary a.& v.

Cranial circumflex humeral a.& v.

Caudal cutaneous antebrachial n.

Musculocutaneous n.

Median n.

Common interosseous a.& v.

Medial cubital v.

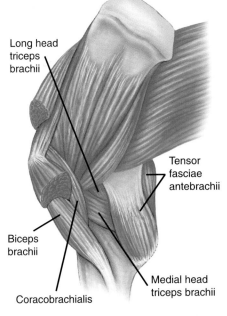

Long head triceps brachii

Tensor fasciae antebrachii

Biceps brachii

Medial head triceps brachii

Coracobrachialis

Medial Muscles of the Right Upper Arm

The *tensor fasciae antebrachii* is a thin sheet of muscle that covers the medial aspect of the triceps brachii. It originates on the caudal border of the scapula and the tendon of the latissimus dorsi muscle. It inserts on the olecranon and the deep fascia of the forearm. Even though the tensor fascia antebrachii crosses both the shoulder joint and the elbow joint, it seems to have very little effect upon the action of each.

Covering the olecranon fossa is a small muscle called the *anconeus*. It

The Neurovascular Supply of the Arm

The radial nerve supplies all of the extensor muscles (triceps brachii, tensor fasciae antebrachii and anconeus) and a small branch innervates part of the brachialis muscle. The musculocutaneous nerve supplies the flexors (the brachialis and the biceps brachii muscles.)

The brachial artery supplies both the biceps brachii and the brachialis. The biceps brachii also receives arterial supply from the anterior radial arteries. The deep brachial artery supplies all three heads of the triceps brachii, the tensor fasciae antebrachii and the anconeus. Branches of the subscapular artery supply the tensor

SUSAN HAKOLA / J. DIRIG

fasciae antebrachii muscle and the long head of the triceps brachii. The ulnar artery also provides some arterial supply to the tensor fasciae antebrachii muscle.

Bony Anatomy of the Radius and Ulna

The forearm consists of the radius and ulna with the corresponding humeroradial or elbow joint. The radius is the larger of the two bones of the forearm. It extends vertically from the articulation with the humerus to the carpus. The bone has a slight curve to it with the convex surface being cranial. The ulna lies caudal to the radius and is usually partially fused to the radius in the adult.

There are two surfaces and two borders within the shaft of the radius. The shaft itself is curved, flattened, narrow in the center and becomes wider at the ends. The dorsal surface is convex in shape whereas the palmer surface is concave. Proximally there is a smooth shallow groove that communicates with the ulna and forms the interosseous space. Located in the lower part of this groove is the nutrient foramen. The tendon of insertion of the brachialis muscle is located at the proximal end of the medial border just dorsal to the medial ligament of the elbow joint.

On the proximal extremity of the radius is the humeral articular surface. This articular surface is traversed by a sagittal ridge and is bounded dorsally by the coronoid process. Immediately distal to this articular surface are two concave facets for articulation with the ulna. Medially, the biceps tendon inserts into the radial tuberosity dorsally. The medial ligament of the elbow joint arises from the medial tuberosity. The common and lateral digital extensor muscles arise from the lateral tuberosity in addition to the lateral ligament of the elbow joint.

The carpal articular surface is located on the distal extremity. There are three parts to this articular surface. A large medial facet that articulates

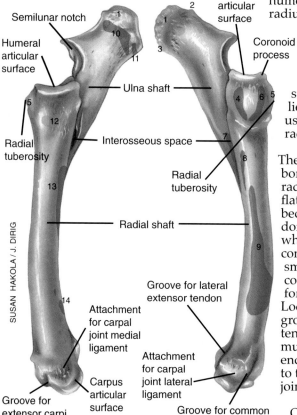

Labels on medial view (left): Semilunar notch, Humeral articular surface, Ulna shaft, Radial tuberosity, Interosseous space, Radial shaft, Groove for lateral extensor tendon, Attachment for carpal joint medial ligament, Attachment for carpal joint lateral ligament, Carpus articular surface, Groove for extensor carpi obliquus tendon, Groove for common extensor tendon

Labels on lateral view (right): Humeral articular surface, Coronoid process, Radial tuberosity

Medial View of the Right Radius and Ulna   **Lateral View of the Right Radius and Ulna**

Key to Insertions & Origins on Radius & Ulna:
1. Insertion of triceps brachii m.
2. Insertion of anconeus m.
3. Insertion of tensor fasciae antebrachii m.
4. Origin of radial head of lateral digital extensor m.
5. Insertion of biceps brachii m.
6. One of radial origins of common digital extensor m.
7. Origin of ulnar head of lateral digital extensor m.
8. One of radial origins of common digital extensor m.
9. Origin of extensor carpi obliquus m.
10. Origin of ulnar head of deep digital flexor m.
11. Ulnar origin of flexor carpi ulnaris m.
12. Insertion of brachialis m.
13. Origin of radial head of deep digital flexor m.
14. Origin of radial head of superior digital flexor m.

SUSAN HAKOLA / J. DIRIG

with the radial carpal bone, an intermediate facet that articulates with the intermediate carpal bone and a lateral facet that articulates with the ulnar carpal bone and the accessory carpal.

There are three grooves on the dorsal surface of the distal extremity. The tendon of the extensor carpi radialis traverses the middle groove, the tendon of the common digital extensor passes laterally and the tendon for the extensor carpi obliquus occupies the medial groove. On both the lateral and medial sides, there are tuberosities which provide a surface for the attachment of the collateral ligaments. The lateral tuberosity contains a groove for the tendon of the lateral extensor muscle.

The ulnar shaft has three sides and at the distal end it tapers to a point. This bone is fused to the radius in the adult from a point below the interosseous space distally. The distal point of the ulna ends with this fusion to the radius at a point just below the middle of the shaft of the radius.

In contrast to the fused distal extremity of the ulna is the proximal extremity which is the most prominent part of this bone. Here, the ulna projects dorsocaudad and forms a lever arm for the extensor muscles of the elbow. Medially, this projection is concave and smooth whereas laterally, the bone is convex and rough. The semilunar notch is formed by a bony projection dorsally (the processus anconeus) and a concave area that provides articulation with the humerus. Just distal to the semilunar notch are two convex facets that provide articulation with the corresponding facets on the proximal end of the radius. The triceps brachii and several other muscles are attached to the olecranon which is the dorsal projection of this proximal extremity.

The Humeroradial or Elbow Joint

The humeroradial joint is a typical ginglymus (hinge) joint in that it is only capable of flexion and extension with a range of motion of 55 to 60 degrees.

55⁰-60⁰

Range of Motion Hinge (Ginglymus) Joint

SUSAN HAKOLA / J. DIRIG

The joint capsule is thin and extends to the olecranon fossa beneath the anconeus muscle. It is adherent to the muscles that arise from the distal humerus and is strengthened on each side by the collateral ligaments. The medial and lateral ligaments attach on each side of the distal humerus at the level of the medial and lateral epicondyles. The ligaments attach to the radius at the level of the medial and lateral tuberosities.

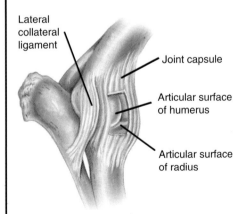

Lateral collateral ligament

Joint capsule

Articular surface of humerus

Articular surface of radius

Lateral View of the Elbow Joint

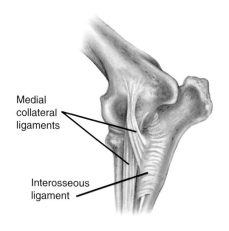

Medial
collateral
ligaments

Interosseous
ligament

SUSAN HAKOLA / J. DIRIG

Medial View of the Elbow Joint

Myology of the Forearm

Basically, the forearm is covered on the cranial, lateral, and caudal surfaces by muscles. The medial surface is covered with subcutaneous tissue. The carpal and digital extensors all originate on the distal craniolateral surfaces of the humerus and travel along the craniolateral portion of the forearm. The exception is the *extensor carpi obliquus*. Carpal and digital flexors all originate from the caudomedial surfaces of the humerus and travel along the caudal surfaces of the forearm.

Unique to this anatomical area is how the insertion tendons of these muscles travel over the carpus distally down the limb. The deep fascia on the dorsal surface of the carpus forms the extensor retinaculum. On the palmer surface, it forms the flexor retinaculum. In each case, the retinaculum guides the tendons over the carpal joint. In addition, each tendon is enclosed within a synovial sheath that begins just above the carpus and extends to well below the carpus.

The largest muscle of the extensor group is the *extensor carpi radialis* which lies on the dorsal surface of the radius. Origination is in the lateral condyle of the humerus and the coronoid fossa. It travels distally to insert on the metacarpal tuberosity. The extensor carpi radialis aids in flexion of the elbow joint but also extends and fixes the carpus.

The *common digital extensor* is actually a compound muscle in that it is composed of two parts. The substantial portion, or the humeral part, originates from the lateral epicondyle of the humerus. It travels distally until the belly of the muscle terminates in a tendon near the distal third of the radius.

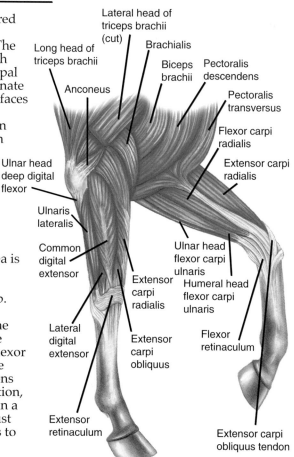

Lateral head of
triceps brachii
(cut)
Brachialis

Long head of
triceps brachii

Biceps   Pectoralis
brachii   descendens

Anconeus

Pectoralis
transversus

Flexor carpi
radialis

Extensor carpi
radialis

Ulnar head
deep digital
flexor

Ulnaris
lateralis

Common
digital
extensor

Ulnar head
flexor carpi
ulnaris

Extensor
carpi
radialis

Humeral head
flexor carpi
ulnaris

Lateral
digital
extensor

Extensor
carpi
obliquus

Flexor
retinaculum

Extensor
retinaculum

Extensor carpi
obliquus tendon

**Musculature of the Forearm,
Lateral and Medial Views**

The tendon then travels distally in the two large grooves on the distal dorsal surface of the radius and over the capsule of the carpal joint. Distally it inserts by merging with the branches of the suspensory ligament at the level of the fetlock. The smaller or radial portion of the common digital extensor arises from the lateral tuberosity and border of the radius. It inserts by fusing with the tendon of the lateral extensor after passing over the carpus in the same sheath as that of the humeral portion. Both portions function to extend the carpal and digital joints and flex the elbow.

The *lateral digital extensor muscle* lies caudal to the common digital extensor and originates on the lateral tuberosity of the radius and the shaft of the ulna. It combines with the common digital extensor at the level of the proximal metacarpal and inserts on the proximal end of the first phalanx. The main function of the lateral digital extensor is to extend the digits and carpus.

The only extensor to originate from the shaft of the radius is the *extensor carpi obliquus*. It travels mediodistally to insert on the head of the second metacarpal bone. This small muscle aids in the extension of the carpal joint.

All of the flexors originate on the humerus and travel along the caudal portion of the forearm. Distal to the actual muscle belly, all tendons of insertion are enclosed within a synovial sheath as they pass across the carpus.

The *flexor carpi radialis* travels along the medial surface of the forearm covering the median vessels and nerves. It originates on the medial condyle of the humerus and inserts on the proximal end of the second metacarpal bone. The primary

function of the flexor carpi radialis is to flex the carpal joint and extend the elbow.

Laterally on the forearm, the *ulnaris lateralis* originates on the lateral epicondyle of the humerus. It travels distally to insert partially on the accessory carpal bone and partially on the proximal extremity of the lateral splint bone. The ulnaris lateralis also functions to flex the carpal joint and extend the elbow.

The *superficial digital flexor* originates on both the medial epicondyle of the humerus and on a ridge on the posterior surface of the radius. The tendon eventually inserts on the proximal end of the second phalanx and the distal end of the first phalanx. The superior check (accessory) ligament, which is purely tendinous, arises from the caudal surface of the radius to merge with the main tendon of the distal surface of the forearm. The superficial digital flexor functions to flex both the digit and carpus and to extend the elbow.

The largest flexor of the forearm is the *deep digital flexor* muscle. It originates in three heads, the humeral head, the ulnar head, and the radial head. The humeral head originates on the medial epicondyle of the humerus whereas the radial head and ulnar heads originate on the proximal radius and ulna, respectively. All the inserting tendons join at the carpus, pass through the carpal canal, and continue distally on the palmar aspect of the limb to insert on the palmar surface of the first phalanx. This tendinous structure is joined in the middle of the metacarpus by the inferior check ligament which is a continuation of the posterior ligament of the carpus. The deep digital flexor functions to flex both the digit and carpus and extend the elbow.

Summary of Muscle Functions

Extensor of the carpus and flexor of the elbow: *Extensor carpi radialis*
Extensor of the carpus: *Extensor carpi obliquus*
Extensors of the carpus and digit: *Common digital extensor* and *Lateral digital extensor*
Flexors of the carpus and extensor of the elbow: *Flexor carpi radialis* and *Ulnaris lateralis*
Flexors of the digits: *Superficial digital flexor* and *Deep digital flexor*

The Superior Check Ligament

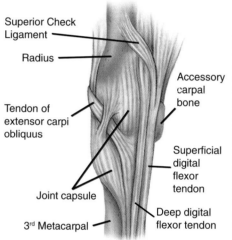

Superior Check Ligament
Radius
Accessory carpal bone
Tendon of extensor carpi obliquus
Superficial digital flexor tendon
Joint capsule
3rd Metacarpal
Deep digital flexor tendon

The radial head of the superficial digital flexor tendon originates from the distal caudomedial surface of the radius. It merges with the main tendon of the superficial digital flexor at the level of the carpus. By definition, it is actually a ligament because, in this section, no muscle tissue is involved.

Neurovascular Supply of the Forearm

The radial nerve supplies all of the extensor group of muscles: the extensor carpi radialis muscle, the common digital extensor, the lateral digital extensor, and the extensor carpi obliquus. In addition, the radial nerve

innervates ulnaris lateralis which is a flexor of the carpal joint. The median nerve supplies the flexor carpi radialis, as well as the superficial and deep digital flexors. Branches of the ulnar nerves also supply the superficial and deep digital flexors.

Arterial supply to the the extensor carpi radialis muscle and the extensor carpi obliquus is provided by the anterior radial arteries. The interosseous artery supplies the common digital extensor, the lateral digital extensor, the ulnaris lateralis, and the extensor carpi obliquus. The median artery supplies the flexor carpi radialis, the ulnaris lateralis, the superficial and the deep digital flexors. The ulnar artery also supplies portions of the deep and superficial digital flexors and the ulnaris lateralis.

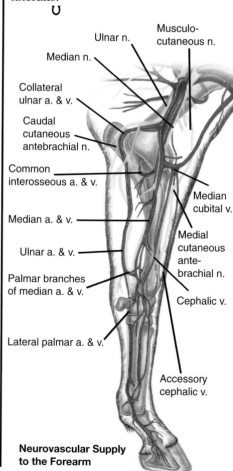

Ulnar n.
Musculo-cutaneous n.
Median n.
Collateral ulnar a. & v.
Caudal cutaneous antebrachial n.
Common interosseous a. & v.
Median a. & v.
Ulnar a. & v.
Palmar branches of median a. & v.
Lateral palmar a. & v.
Median cubital v.
Medial cutaneous ante-brachial n.
Cephalic v.
Accessory cephalic v.

Neurovascular Supply to the Forearm

The Bony Anatomy of the Carpus

This anatomical area is referred to as the "knee." It is composed of two rows of bones and three joints. The proximal row of bones, from medial to lateral, are the radial, intermediate, ulnar, and accessory carpal bones. The distal or metacarpal row from medial to lateral are the first, second, third, and fourth carpal bones.

The radial carpal bone is the largest of the proximal row and is clearly six-sided. The proximal surface articulates with the medial facet on the distal radius. Its distal surface articulates with the second and third carpal bones and the lateral surface articulates with the intermediate carpal bone.

The intermediate carpal bone is wider in front than behind and is in the shape of a wedge. The proximal articulation is with the middle facet of the distal radius. Distally, the intermediate carpal bone articulates with the third and fourth carpal bones. Laterally, it articulates with the ulnar carpal and medially, with the radial carpal bone.

The smallest bone in the proximal row is the ulnar carpal bone. Laterally, there is not an articulation. Medially, it articulates with the lateral facet on the distal radius and distally, with the fourth carpal bone.

The accessory carpal does not withstand any of the weight bearing forces. It is located caudal to the ulnar bone and the lateral portion of the distal radius. Medially, it is concave in shape and forms the lateral wall of the carpal groove. Dorsally, there are two facets for articulation. The proximal facet articulates with the lateral facet on the distal radius. Distally, there is an articulation with the ulnar carpal bone.

The first carpal bone of the distal row is a small pea-shaped bone that is only present in 50% of the horses. It can even be present in one limb and not the other. The first carpal bone is embedded in the distal portion of the medial ligament caudal to the second carpal bone.

The second carpal bone is the smallest in the distal row that is constant in appearance. Proximally, it articulates with the radial carpal. The lateral articulation involves three facets with the third carpal bone. Distally, the

Dorsal View Left Forelimb

Radial carpal
Radius
Second carpal
Third carpal
Second metacarpal

Palmer View Left Forelimb

Accessory carpal
Intermediate carpal
Ulnar carpal
Fourth carpal
Fourth metacarpal
Second metacarpal
Third metacarpal

Intermediate carpal
Radial carpal
Third carpal
Second carpal

SUSAN HAKOLA / J. DIRIG

Lateral View Left Carpus

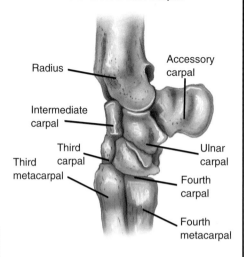

Radius

Accessory carpal

Intermediate carpal

Third carpal

Third metacarpal

Ulnar carpal

Fourth carpal

Fourth metacarpal

Medial View Left Carpus

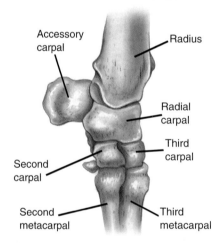

Accessory carpal

Radius

Radial carpal

Third carpal

Second carpal

Second metacarpal

Third metacarpal

the third carpal bone. Distally, the second carpal bone articulates mainly with the second metacarpal bone but also has a small articular surface for the third metacarpal bone.

The third carpal bone forms 2/3 of the distal row and is, therefore, the largest of this row. Proximally, it articulates with the radial and intermediate carpal bones. The distal articulation is almost exclusively with the third metacarpal bone, but there is a small facet medially for the second metacarpal. Medially, the third carpal bone articulates with the second

carpal and laterally, it articulates with the fourth.

Proximally, the fourth carpal articulates with both the intermediate and ulnar carpal bones. Distally, it articulates with the third and fourth metacarpals. Medially, it articulates with the third carpal bone.

The Bony Anatomy of the Metacarpus

The largest of the metacarpal bones, the third metacarpal, is one of the strongest bones in the skeleton. It is composed of a thick, compact cortex that is thicker on the medial and cranial surfaces with very little spongy substance to this bone. Proximally, it articulates with the distal row of the carpus. Distally, it articulates with the first phalanx and the proximal sesamoid bones.

The small metacarpal bones, the second and fourth, are not well developed and occur on each side of the third metacarpal to form the metacarpal groove. Proximally, the medial, or second metacarpal, articulates with the second and third carpal bone. The lateral, or the fourth metacarpal, articulates with the fourth carpal bone. Both the second and the fourth metacarpals also articulate with the third metacarpal. Distally, the second and fourth metacarpals end in small nodules that occur 2/3 to 3/4 of the way down the third metacarpal, depending on the individual. The interosseous metacarpal ligament unites the shafts of the third metacarpal with the shafts of the second and the fourth metacarpals. As the animal ages, this ligament undergoes ossification.

The Carpal Articulations

The knee is actually composed of three joints. The proximal joint is the radiocarpal joint, a ginglymus joint, with an angle of opening almost 90 degrees. The intercarpal joint opens to almost 70 degrees and the carpometacarpal joint, being an arthrodial type joint, does not open at all.

The fibrous joint capsule is common to all three joints. It extends proximally from the articulations with the radius to the distal articulations with the metacarpals. Deeply, it covers the carpal bones and the many small ligaments. Anteriorly, it forms the dorsal carpal ligament in addition to the canals for the extensor tendons. On the palmar surface, the joint capsule forms the dorsal surface of the carpal canal. It continues distally to form the inferior check ligament that goes on to merge with the deep digital flexor at the middle of the metacarpus.

The three joints are lined with three synovial membranes. The intercarpal and carpometacarpal synovial sac communicate between the third and fourth carpal bones. The radiocarpal

synovial membrane exists as its own separate entity.

Laterally and medially, the carpus is stabilized by two ligaments. They both arise from the medial and lateral tuberosities of the radius to attach to the second, third, and fourth metacarpal bone. The first carpal bone, when it exists, is embedded within the fibers of the medial ligament.

As the tendons pass over the carpus, they are surrounded by thin walled, fluid-filled tubes to protect them from wear. There are only two tendons that are not enveloped: the short tendon of the ulnaris lateralis and the tendon of the carpi ulnaris muscle. One of the most significant of these tendon synovial sheaths is the carpal synovial sheath. It encloses the superficial and deep digital flexor tendons as they pass through the carpal canal.

Lateral View Right Carpus

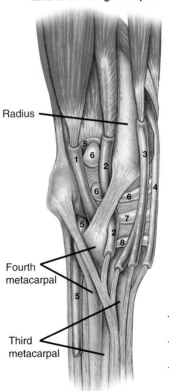

Radius

Fourth metacarpal

Third metacarpal

1. Tendon sheath ulnaris lateralis
2. Tendon sheath lateral digital extensor
3. Tendon sheath common digital extensor
4. Tendon sheath extensor carpi radialis
5. Tendon sheath superficial and deep digital flexors
6. Radiocarpal joint capsule
7. Midcarpal joint capsule
8. Carpometacarpal joint capsule
9. Tendon sheath extensor carpi obliquus
10. Tendon sheath extensor carpi radialis
11. Tendon sheath flexor carpi radialis
12. Carpal synovial sheath

Medial View Right Carpus

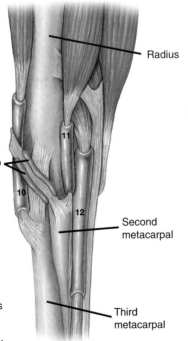

Radius

Second metacarpal

Third metacarpal

SUSAN HAKOLA / J. DIRIG

The tendon sheaths of the lateral digital extensor, the common digital extensor, the extensor carpi radialis, the superficial and deep digital flexors, and the long tendon of the ulnaris lateralis occur laterally. On the medial surface, the tendon sheaths of the extensor carpi obliquus, the extensor carpi radialis, and the flexor carpi radialis can be visualized.

Movement of the Carpal Joints

Flexion of the radiocarpal joint and the intercarpal joint is accomplished by a combined effort of the flexor carpi radialis, the flexor carpi ulnaris, and the ulnaris lateralis muscles. The extensor carpi radialis and the extensor carpi obliquus muscles allow extension of these joints.

The structure of the carpal bones prevent an overextension of the radiocarpal and intercarpal joints. These bones are flattened over their articular surfaces and are connected by the palmar carpal ligament.

The superior and inferior check ligaments provide stability to the carpal joint during motion. The superior check ligament originates from the distal caudomedial surface of the radius and travels distally to merge with the tendon of the superficial digital flexor. The inferior check ligament travels distally from the palmar carpal ligament to join the deep digital flexor tendon at the midshaft area of the metacarpus. These check ligaments provide support palmarly, whereas the tendon of the extensor carpi radialis stabilizes the extended carpus dorsally.

Anatomy of the Suspensory Ligament

The suspensory ligament is located on the palmar surface of the third metacarpal between the second and fourth metacarpal bones. Proximally, it is attached to the posterior surface of the third metacarpal and the

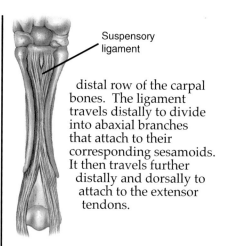

Suspensory ligament

distal row of the carpal bones. The ligament travels distally to divide into abaxial branches that attach to their corresponding sesamoids. It then travels further distally and dorsally to attach to the extensor tendons.

Anatomy of the Inferior Check Ligament

The inferior check ligament is a continuation of the volar carpal ligament distally, where it blends with the deep digital flexor tendon at the midshaft area of the metacarpal. It is approximately the same width as the deep digital flexor tendon.

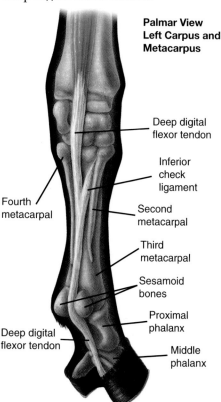

**Palmar View
Left Carpus and
Metacarpus**

Deep digital flexor tendon

Inferior check ligament

Fourth metacarpal

Second metacarpal

Third metacarpal

Sesamoid bones

Proximal phalanx

Deep digital flexor tendon

Middle phalanx

The Neurovascular Supply of the Carpus and Metacarpus

The region of the carpus and the metacarpus receives innervation from three nerves. The medial cutaneous antebrachial nerve supplies the dorsomedial areas. The dorsolateral areas are supplied by the dorsal branches of the ulnar nerve. The palmar areas are innervated by the medial and lateral palmar nerves.

The deep antebrachial vessels give rise to the proximal radial artery and the radial vessels just proximal to the carpus. The median artery gives off a palmar branch just before it enters the carpal canal. A branch from the radial artery merges with the median artery and this union forms the medial palmar artery. The lateral palmar artery is formed from the palmar branch of the median artery and the collateral ulnar artery proximal to the carpus.

The medial and radial arteries form an arch just distal to the carpus. Originating from this arch are the medial and lateral palmar metacarpal arteries. These travel distally on the axial surface of the second and fourth metacarpals.

U

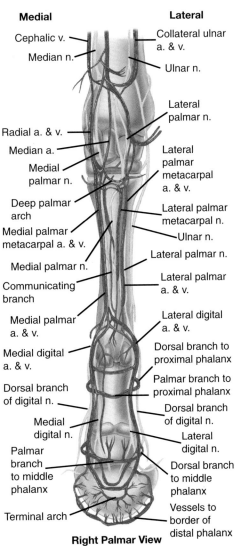

SUSAN HAKOLA / J. DIRIG

Left Medial View

- Ulnar a. & v.
- Palmar branches of median a. & v.
- Lateral palmar nerve
- Accessory cephalic v.
- Radial a.
- Medial palmar n.
- Medial dorsal metacarpal a.
- Lateral palmar a., v., & n.
- Medial palmar a., v., & n.
- Lateral palmar a. & v. (lateral & palmer to metacarpal)
- Dorsal branch of medial digital n.
- Medial digital n.

Medial

- Cephalic v.
- Median n.
- Radial a. & v.
- Median a.
- Medial palmar n.
- Deep palmar arch
- Medial palmar metacarpal a. & v.
- Medial palmar n.
- Communicating branch
- Medial palmar a. & v.
- Medial digital a. & v.
- Dorsal branch of digital n.
- Medial digital n.
- Palmar branch to middle phalanx
- Terminal arch

Lateral

- Collateral ulnar a. & v.
- Ulnar n.
- Lateral palmar n.
- Lateral palmar metacarpal a. & v.
- Lateral palmar metacarpal n.
- Ulnar n.
- Lateral palmar n.
- Lateral palmar a. & v.
- Lateral digital a. & v.
- Dorsal branch to proximal phalanx
- Palmar branch to proximal phalanx
- Dorsal branch of digital n.
- Lateral digital n.
- Dorsal branch to middle phalanx
- Vessels to border of distal phalanx

Right Palmar View

Bony Anatomy of the Fetlock and Pastern

The metacarpalphalangeal joint is a ginglymus joint formed by the distal end of the third metacarpal bone, the proximal end of the first phalanx, and the proximal sesamoid bones. The articular surface of the third metacarpal bone is cylindrically curved and is divided into two slightly unequal parts by a sagittal ridge. This articulates with the proximal first phalanx and the two proximal sesamoids. The joint capsule is attached along the margins of the articular surfaces. When the animal is in the standing position, the fetlock is in a state of partial dorsal flexion. The natural range of motion of this joint, through the functions of flexion and extension, is 140 degrees.

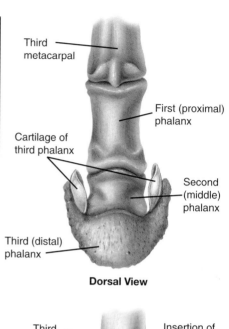

Third metacarpal

First (proximal) phalanx

Cartilage of third phalanx

Second (middle) phalanx

Third (distal) phalanx

Dorsal View

Lateral View

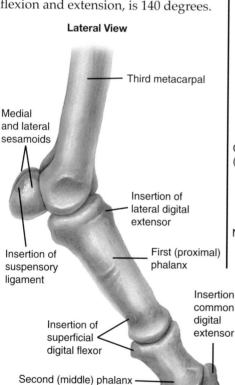

Third metacarpal

Medial and lateral sesamoids

Insertion of lateral digital extensor

Insertion of suspensory ligament

First (proximal) phalanx

Insertion of superficial digital flexor

Insertion common digital extensor

Second (middle) phalanx

Third (distal) phalanx

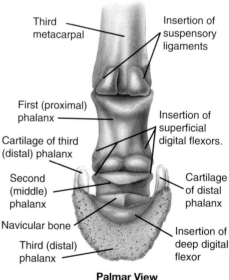

Third metacarpal

Insertion of suspensory ligaments

First (proximal) phalanx

Insertion of superficial digital flexors.

Cartilage of third (distal) phalanx

Second (middle) phalanx

Cartilage of distal phalanx

Navicular bone

Third (distal) phalanx

Insertion of deep digital flexor

Palmar View

140° range of motion hinge (ginglymus) joint

SUSAN HAKOLA / J. DIRIG

The first phalanx is a long compact bone that is situated between the third metacarpal bone and the second phalanx or short pastern bone. It has a shaft and two articular surfaces. This bone is obliquely oriented at an angle of 55 degrees downward and forward in a well conformed limb. The proximal articular surface is greater medially than laterally. Distally, the articular surface contains a trochlea for articulation with the second phalanx. The medial articular surface is slightly larger in area than the lateral. This is delineated by a shallow sagittal groove between the two condyles.

The second phalanx is oriented in the horizontal direction in the same manner as the first phalanx. Proximally, it articulates with the first phalanx with two glenoid cavities separated by a low ridge. The distal surface is trochlear in nature and articulates with the third phalanx and the navicular bone. The dorsal surface is convex with a roughened surface that serves as an attachment for ligamentous structures. The volar surface is smooth and flattened.

Each proximal sesamoid has the appearance of a three-sided triangle. The sesamoids are located behind the distal end of the third metacarpal bone. There is an articular surface that corresponds to the distal end of the third metacarpal bone. It has a flexor surface between the two bones that is lined with cartilage to provide a smooth groove for the deep digital flexor tendon. There is an abaxial surface that is concave and attaches to the suspensory ligament. The sesamoids also have both an apex and base.

Insertion Sites for the Muscles

1. The *lateral digital extensor* inserts on the proximal extremity of the first phalanx.
2. The *common digital extensor* has two areas of insertion. The extensor process of the third phalanx is the main area of insertion with some fibers inserting on the dorsal surfaces

of the first and second phalanges.
3. The *superficial digital flexor* inserts behind the collateral ligaments on the proximal extremity of the second phalanx and the distal extremity of the first phalanx.
4. The *deep digital flexor* inserts in a broad area along the semilunar crest and adjacent surface of the cartilage of the third phalanx.
5. The *suspensory ligament* is attached to the abaxial surfaces of the sesamoid bones.

Ligamentous Structures of the Fetlock and Pastern

The large bones of the fetlock are connected by medial and lateral collateral ligaments. These are divided into a superficial and deep layer. The superficial layer originates on the distal end of the third metacarpal bone to insert onto the articular surface of the first phalanx. The deep layer originates on the distal end of the metacarpal bone and travels to insert on the abaxial surface of the sesamoid and the proximal end of the first phalanx.

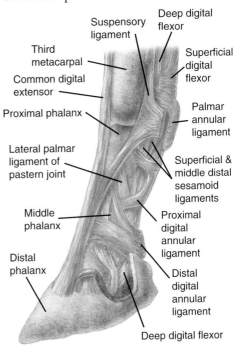

Suspensory ligament
Deep digital flexor
Third metacarpal
Superficial digital flexor
Common digital extensor
Proximal phalanx
Palmar annular ligament
Lateral palmar ligament of pastern joint
Superficial & middle distal sesamoid ligaments
Middle phalanx
Proximal digital annular ligament
Distal phalanx
Distal digital annular ligament
Deep digital flexor

SUSAN HAKOLA

Lateral View

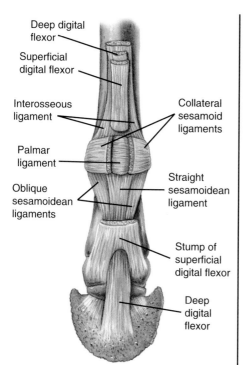

Deep digital flexor

Superficial digital flexor

Interosseous ligament

Collateral sesamoid ligaments

Palmar ligament

Oblique sesamoidean ligaments

Straight sesamoidean ligament

Stump of superficial digital flexor

Deep digital flexor

Palmar View

SUSAN HAKOLA / J. DIRIG

The suspensory ligament, or interosseous tendon, lies in the metacarpal groove. It divides into two diverging branches just dorsal to the fetlock. Each branch attaches to the abaxial face of the corresponding sesamoid. It continues to travel distocraniad to the dorsal surface of the first phalanx. Here, the suspensory ligament combines with the extensor tendons.

The flexor tendons are held in place by large annular ligaments that are thickenings of the deep fascia. The annular ligament of the fetlock, or palmar annular ligament, arises from the abaxial borders of the sesamoids and stabilizes the flexor tendons, especially the superficial flexor tendon. The proximal digital annular ligament forms an "X" when viewed posteriorly. The corners attach to the proximal and distal tubercles, which are knoblike elevations. This ligament holds the flexor tendons against the ligaments on the palmar surface of the first phalanx. The distal digital annular ligament arises medially and laterally on the proximal phalanx to insert on the distal phalanx between the deep flexor tendon and the digital cushion.

There are three sites of sesamoidean ligaments. The intersesamoidean ligament connects both sesamoids together and extends dorsally to help form the articular surface of the fetlock joint. Both the lateral and medial collateral sesamoid ligaments arise on the abaxial surface of each sesamoid. The collateral ligaments pass cranially to divide into two branches that insert on the distal end of the third metacarpal and the proximal end of the first phalanx.

There are three distal sesamoidean ligaments. The superficial ligament arises at the base of the sesamoids and the intersesamoid ligament to insert on the proximal end of the second phalanx. The middle distal sesamoidean ligament also originates at the base of the sesamoids and intersesamoidean ligament to insert onto the first phalanx. The cruciate sesamoidean ligaments both arise at the base of the sesamoid, cross each other, and insert on the proximal end of the first phalanx.

Vascular Supply to the Fetlock and Pastern

At the level of the fetlock, between the digital flexor tendons and the suspensory ligament, the medial palmar vein and artery form an arch with the lateral palmar vein and artery. It is from this point that the medial and palmar digital veins and arteries arise. A superficial palmar arch is formed by an anastomoses of the vessels from the distal deep palmar arch and the vessels from the lateral digital artery and vein. The arterial supply and venous drainage of the fetlock joint is provided from branches of this arch.

The extensor and flexor tendons, the digital synovial sheath, the ligaments and the superficial surfaces of the

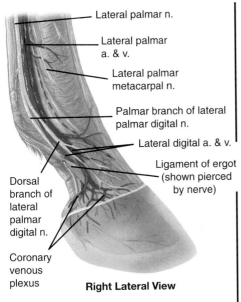

Lateral palmar n.

Lateral palmar a. & v.

Lateral palmar metacarpal n.

Palmar branch of lateral palmar digital n.

Lateral digital a. & v.

Ligament of ergot (shown pierced by nerve)

Dorsal branch of lateral palmar digital n.

Coronary venous plexus

Right Lateral View

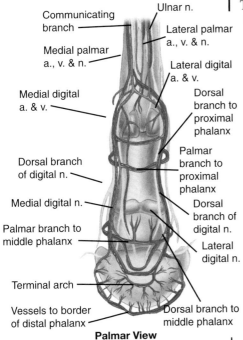

Communicating branch

Medial palmar a., v. & n.

Medial digital a. & v.

Dorsal branch of digital n.

Medial digital n.

Palmar branch to middle phalanx

Terminal arch

Vessels to border of distal phalanx

Ulnar n.

Lateral palmar a., v. & n.

Lateral digital a. & v.

Dorsal branch to proximal phalanx

Palmar branch to proximal phalanx

Dorsal branch of digital n.

Lateral digital n.

Dorsal branch to middle phalanx

Palmar View

The first phalanx and its surrounding structures are supplied vascularly by a palmar branch of the digital artery that also gives off a dorsal branch. The vessels from these dorsal and palmar branches form an anastomosis in this area which provides a circular supply and drainage. The palmar branch travels between the first phalanx and the flexor tendons to anastomose with the vessels originating from the straight and oblique distal sesamoidean ligaments. The dorsal branch anastomoses with the vessels arising deep to the common digital extensor tendon.

At the level of the second phalanx, the dorsal vessels that originate from the digital vasculature form common anastomoses deep to the extensor tendons. These vessels supply and drain the common digital extensor tendon, the fascia, and the skin. They send branches to the coffin joint and the periopic and coronary corium. The palmar vessels, at the level of the second phalanx, along with a branch from the digital vasculature, form an arch. Branches from this arch provide nutrients to the second phalanx.

Neurological Supply to the Fetlock and Pastern

At the level of the fetlock, the medial and lateral palmar nerves give rise to the medial and lateral palmar digital nerves. Both of these medial and lateral palmar digital nerves immediately send off dorsal branches. The skin, the dorsal portion of the fetlock joint, and the interphalangeal joints are all supplied from these branches.

The palmar digital nerve is the main supply of the fetlock joint capsule. This nerve then travels distally to supply the skin, the distal sesamoidean ligaments and the pastern joint capsule.

U

fetlock joint are supplied and drained by the digital arteries and veins.

Anatomy of the Equine Forefoot

The forefoot of the horse is a product of evolution and a miracle in bioengineering. It is extremely light in weight, flexible, and yet it withstands constant, concussive forces. Growth is from the dorsal surface, whereas tissue loss due to friction or abrasive forces occurs on the ground surface.

The forefoot consists of the epidermal hoof itself, the connective tissue or dermal layer (dermis), the digital cushion, the distal phalanx (which is called the coffin bone), the lateral cartilages of the digital phalanx, the distal interphalangeal joint or coffin joint, the distal extremity of the short pastern bone, the navicular bone, the navicular bursa, several ligaments, the tendons of insertion of the common digital extensor and deep digital flexor tendons, and numerous blood vessels and nerves.

Layers of the Hoof

Histologically, the wall is made up of the following three layers: the stratum externum, the stratum medium, and the stratum internum. These three layers arise from the epithelium covering the coronary dermis.

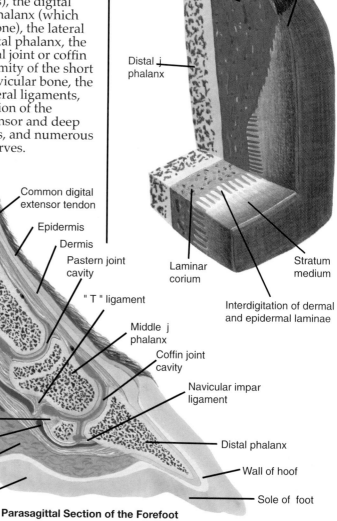

Layers of the Hoof

- Tubular horn of stratum medium
- Periople
- Distal phalanx
- Laminar corium
- Stratum medium
- Interdigitation of dermal and epidermal laminae

Proximal phalanx
Common digital extensor tendon
Superficial digital flexor tendon
Epidermis
Dermis
Pastern joint cavity
"T" ligament
Middle phalanx
Coffin joint cavity
Deep digital flexor tendon
Navicular bone
Navicular impar ligament
Navicular bursa
Distal phalanx
Digital cushion
Wall of hoof
Frog
Sole of foot

SUSAN HAKOLA

Parasagittal Section of the Forefoot

The periople is the soft, white, horny tissue that communicates the epithelial hoof wall with the epidermis of the skin at the coronet. In this fashion, it ultimately contributes to the stratum external of the wall. This external layer is an extremely thin layer of tubular horn covering the entire surface of the wall. This periople expands caudally on the ground surface of the foot over the bulbs of the heel. It also contains two layers, a granular cell layer (or stratum granulosum) and a superficial layer covering the rest of the wall, referred to as a stratum tectorium. The stratum tectorium reduces evaporative water loss from the foot and gives the wall its smooth, glossy appearance.

The middle layer, or stratum medium, consists of a very thick, hard layer of tubular and intertubular horn. The proximal portion divides to form the coronary groove, in which lies the convex coronary corium. The surface of the coronary groove has numerous openings into which fit the papillae of the overlying coronary corium. It is pigmented when the hoof is dark. This middle portion actually comprises the bulk of the hoof wall. The spaces between the horn tubules are filled with intertubular horns. The tubules themselves originate from the germinal epidermis that covers the lateral and distal borders of the dermal papillae since the stratum medium is devoid of a granulosum layer histologically. The inner tubular horn originates from the germinal epidermis between the papillae. The papillae in this region are elongated and are oriented perpendicular to the ground surface.

The internal layer or the stratum internum (lamellatum) is always non-pigmented and consists of many keratinized primary epidermal lamellae which extend from the coronary groove to the ground surface. Each primary epidermal lamellae bears 100 to 150 non-keratinized secondary epidermal lamellae. These each interdigitate with the primary and secondary lamellae of the lamellar corium.

Regions of the Hoof

The epidermal wall is that part of the hoof which is visible to the eye when the horse is standing on the ground. Topographically, it is divided into three regions: the toe, the medial and lateral quarters, and the heels. The heels of the wall are reflected inwards and form the bars which are separated from the frog by the paracuneal grooves. The wall is thickest at the toe, and gradually thins towards the heel.

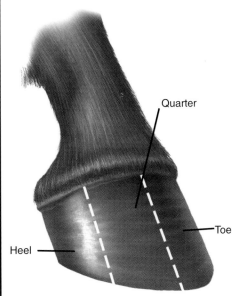

Quarter

Heel

Toe

SUSAN HAKOLA / J. DIRIG

Regions of the Hoof Wall

A Palmar View of the Hoof

The sole is what comprises the greater part of the ground surface of the hoof. It fills the entire space between the wall and the frog. It is slightly concave so that only the distal edge of the wall makes contact on firm ground. The areas between the bars, in the quarters of the hoof, are known as the angles of the sole. This is where one finds corns.

The junction between the sole and the wall is known as the white line (zona alba). It is composed of the non-pigmented stratum medium of the wall and a pigmented portion produced by the stratum germinativum dorsal to the papillae on the distal parts of the laminar corium.

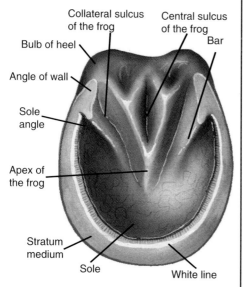

Sole of a Trimmed Foot

The frog projects into the sole area from the posterior area of the hoof. It is a wedge-shaped mass that occupies the angle bounded by the bars and extends into the sole cranially. The frog is separated from the bars and the sole by deep paracuneal grooves that accentuate its medial and lateral borders. It is within these grooves that the condition known as "thrush" is located.

The frog itself is tubular, fairly soft and elastic. It is kept this way by a fatty secretion from glands in the underlying digital cushion. A sound hoof requires frog pressure or contact with the ground with every step.

Concussion to the foot is absorbed by the frog from two directions. Concussive force resulting from impact on the ground is absorbed directly by the rubbery tissue of the frog. Concussive forces that descend distally through the foot from the

pastern are redirected through the plantar cushion to the lateral cartilages and hoof.

When there is no pressure on the frog, contracted heels will result. Compression from the pastern bones upon the plantar cushion acts to draw the lateral cartilages inward without an opposing impact force to counter. This eventually allows contraction of the heels.

The Corium

The dermis, which is deep to the hoof, can be divided into five parts: the perioplic corium, the coronary corium, the lamellar corium, the corium of the sole, and the corium of the frog.

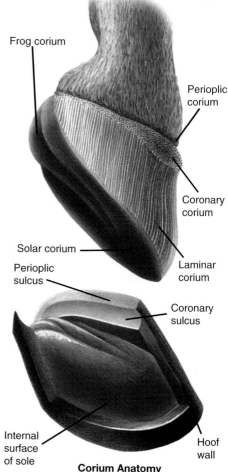

Corium Anatomy

The perioplic corium is a narrow light-colored band of corium that is found at the coronet deep to the periople. This area, like the rest of the dermis, is filled with short papillae. The periople is nourished by the perioplic corium.

The stratum germinativum lies dorsal to the perioplic corium and produces the horn of the periople. When there is growth within the wall, the periople is carried distally to form the stratum tectorium.

Immediately below the perioplic corium is the thick corium known as the coronary corium. The coronary dermis is separated from the periople dermis by the shallow coronary groove. This coronary dermis follows the coronet. Like the hoof wall, it folds upon itself above the heels. This is what is commonly termed the coronary band. The epithelium that covers most of its surface produces the bulk of the wall.

Composed of about 600 sensitive derminal lamellae that interdigitate with the insensitive horny lamellae on the deep surface of the wall, is a layer that is referred to as the lamellae

dermis. Both the sensitive and the insensitive lamellae bear numerous secondary lamellae which further secure the wall to the dermis. This is then secured to the coffin bone, suspending it within the hoof capsule.

The Laminae

The terms sensitive and insensitive laminae need to be defined. The insensitive laminae are the keratinized portions of the primary epidermal laminae. The sensitive portions involve the stratum germinativum that includes all of the secondary epidermal laminae and the laminar corium. The sensitive lamina has the largest surface area of the sensitive structures. It covers the coffin bone, the lateral portions of the distal half of the lateral cartilages and travels inward at the heels to form the sensitive portion of the bars.

There is an interdigitation of the sensitive laminae and the horny laminae of the wall. These horny laminae line the entire inner surface of the hoof wall. Therefore, since the sensitive laminae are attached to the coffin bone, the entire animal

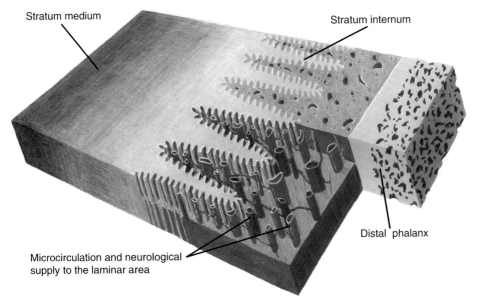

Stratum medium

Stratum internum

Distal phalanx

Microcirculation and neurological supply to the laminar area

SUSAN HAKOLA

Interdigitation of Dermal and Epidermal Laminae

is suspended from the hoof wall by these interdigitating layers. This area of interdigitation of sensitive and insensitive layers is where the damage occurs during the condition of founder or laminitis.

There are both primary and secondary laminae that provide support to the animals suspended weight. Approximately 600 primary laminae are visible to the naked eye. Microscopically there are another 100 secondary laminae that are arranged perpendicularly to each primary laminae. The weight of the animal is then distributed over 60,000 attachments when these are considered biomechanically in unison. Within this laminar attachment, the average horse has approximately eight square feet of area for the attachment of the hoof to the bone. This amounts to about 4 ounces per square inch of attachment when the animal is supporting its entire weight on one foot during the support phase of the stride.

Growth of the hoof wall towards the ground surface originates from the stratum germinativum of the coronary epidermis. The growth of the wall is approximately 6mm per month, with growth being slower in a cold, dry environment. The hoof wall arises equally distal to the coronary epidermis; therefore, the youngest portion of the hoof is located at the heels. This youngest portion is also the most elastic which allows the heels to expand during impact thus softening some degree of the concussion.

The corium of the sole supplies the nutrition to the horny sole. It is sometimes pigmented and bears large papillae that are larger along the convex borders and angles. On the deep surface, it is attached to the surface of the third phalanx by a vascular periosteum.

The corium of the frog consists of small papillae and lies deep to the insensitive frog. It communicates

with the digital cushion and it provides nutrition to the frog.

Neurovascular Anatomy

The vascular supply to the dermis comes from three sets of vessels, all branches of the digital arteries, that descend into the hoof on each side of the flexor tendons. Those branches that arise at the level of the coronet supply the perioplic and coronary dermis. Those that originate opposite the pastern joint supply branches to the digital cushion and the dermis of the caudal aspect of the hoof, including the frog. The vessels from the third set arise from the dorsal and palmar terminal branches and go to the laminella and sole branches. The venous supply does not correspond to that of the arterial supply. Instead, it forms an extensive interconnecting network in the dermis and underlying subcutis, particularly in the coronary band area.

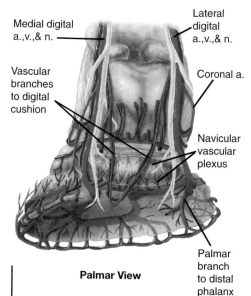

Medial digital a.,v.,& n.

Lateral digital a.,v.,& n.

Vascular branches to digital cushion

Coronal a.

Navicular vascular plexus

Palmar View

Palmar branch to distal phalanx

On the medial surface, at the level of the fetlock, the medial palmar nerve gives rise to the medial digital nerve. Dorsal branches arise to serve the dorsal area of the foot. At the level of the pastern joint, a branch is given off to serve the digital cushion. Laterally, the lateral palmar nerve descends to the level of the fetlock to become the lateral digital nerve. This nerve varies very little from its medial counterpart. There is a communicating branch between the lateral and medial palmar nerves that should be considered when blocking the limb with local anesthetics.

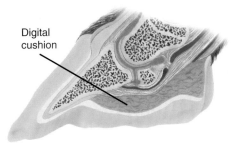

Digital cushion

cushion is adherent to the terminal part of the deep digital flexor tendon.

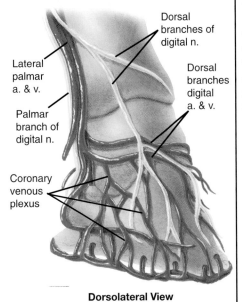

Dorsal branches of digital n.

Lateral palmar a. & v.

Dorsal branches digital a. & v.

Palmar branch of digital n.

Coronary venous plexus

Dorsolateral View

The Digital Cushion

The digital cushion is a wedge-shaped mass that overlies the frog. It has four surfaces, a base and an apex. The deep surface actually faces dorsocraniad and is connected with the distal fibrous sheath of the deep flexor tendon. The superficial surface covers the corium of the frog. The sides of the digital cushion are opposed to the cartilages of the third phalanx. Distally, the digital cushion is opposed to these cartilages in a rich, venous plexus. The base, situated posteriorly, is partly subcutaneous. It is divided by a central depression into two rounded prominences that are called the bulbs of the cushion. The apex of the digital

The Coffin Bone

The third phalanx, or coffin bone, is entirely enclosed by the hoof. It is referred to as the coffin bone because its anatomical position in the hoof is as if the bone were placed within a coffin. The general shape of the bone conforms to the hoof itself. It includes three surfaces, three borders and two angles.

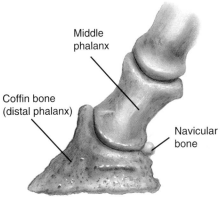

Middle phalanx

Coffin bone (distal phalanx)

Navicular bone

SUSAN HAKOLA / J. DIRIG

The articular surfaces face dorsally and caudally and are chiefly opposed to the distal surface of the second phalanx. Along the volar border, it also articulates with the distal sesamoid or navicular bone. The dorsal, or wall surface, slopes cranio-distad at an angle of inclination parallel to that of the hoof wall. The surface of this dorsal wall is rough, porous and contains numerous foramina due to the vascularity found in these tissues. The volar or palmar surface is arched and divided into two unequal parts by a curved rough line, the semilunar crest. The area cranial to the crest is crescent-shaped, concave, and comparatively smooth as it corresponds intimately with the overlying tissues. The portion behind the crest is much smaller and semilunar. It is intimately related to the deep digital flexor tendon.

The proximal or coronary border bears a central eminence which is called the extensor process where the common extensor tendon attaches. On either side is a depression for the attachment of the collateral ligaments. The distal border is thin, sharp and irregularly notched. There is commonly a wider notch over the cranial apex. The angles of the coffin bone are masses which project caudally on either side. The medial one usually projects a shorter distance. Each one of these angles is divided into an upper and lower part by a notch that is perforated by foramina that lead to the dorsal groove. The proximal border of these angles carries the cartilage.

The cartilages of the coffin bone are curved plates which surmount the angles on either side. They are large and extend above the margin of the hoof sufficiently to be palpable.

Anatomy of the Navicular Bone

The navicular bone or distal sesamoid is shuttle-shaped and is situated behind the junction of the second and third phalanges. It has an articular

Navicular Bone

surface which faces craniodorsad and a flexor surface which faces distocaudad. The proximal border is wide, grooved in the middle, and

rounded on either side. The distal border bears a narrow facet in the front for articulation with the third phalanx. Behind this groove are a large number of foramina for vascular supply.

The bursa podotrochlearis, (or navicular bursa,) is located between the deep digital flexor tendon and the navicular bone. The function of this bursa is to provide a lubricated surface for the movement of the flexor tendon.

The Distal Interphalangeal Joint

This distal interphalangeal joint or articulation is a ginglymus joint formed by the junction of the second and third phalanges and the distal sesamoid bone. The chief movement of this joint is flexion and extension. In the standing position, the joint is extended. During volar flexion, a very small amount of lateral movement and rotation can be produced upon manipulation of the hoof. There are two articular surfaces: the surface on the proximal end of the coffin bone that articulates with the second phalanx, and the surface behind that which articulates with the navicular bone.

Ligaments Within the Hoof

There are four major ligaments found within the equine hoof. They are the medial and lateral ligaments, the medial and lateral collateral ligaments of the coffin joint, the medial and lateral collateral ligaments of the navicular, and the short unpaired distal impar ligament.

The medial and lateral ligaments extend from each phalanx to the cartilages of the distal phalanx. The medial and lateral collateral ligaments of the coffin joint extend between the distal end of the middle phalanx and the depressions on the respective sides of each coffin bone.

The medial and lateral collateral
ligaments of the navicular bone
extend between the distal extremity
of the proximal phalanx and the two
extremities along the proximal border
of the navicular bone. The singular
impar ligament extends between the
distal border of the navicular bone
and the palmar surface of the distal
phalanx.

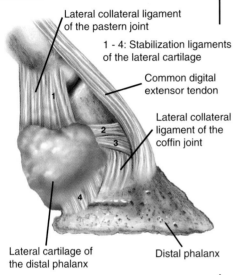

Lateral collateral ligament
of the pastern joint

1 - 4: Stabilization ligaments
of the lateral cartilage

Common digital
extensor tendon

Lateral collateral
ligament of the
coffin joint

Lateral cartilage of
the distal phalanx

Distal phalanx

Ligaments Within the Hoof

There are two tendons that are
enclosed by the hoof. The common
digital extensor tendon inserts on the
extensor process of the distal phalanx.
The deep digital flexor tendon inserts
on the semilunar crest of the distal
phalanx. The navicular bursa lies
between the deep digital flexor tendon
and the navicular bone just prior to its
insertion.

∪

Anatomy of the Pelvis

The hindlimb may be divided into six different segments. They are: the pelvic girdle, the femur, the leg (which includes the tibia, fibula, patella and the stifle joint,) the hock, the metatarsus, the fetlock, and phalanges. Even though the hindlimb supports only forty percent of the body weight of the horse, the greater part of the forward impetus for locomotion originates here. The pelvic limb is much more stable than that of the shoulder attachment to the axial skeleton. The hindlimb is attached to the axial skeleton at the sacrum and the sacroiliac joint, versus the more unstable synarthrosis and ligamentous joints involved in the forelimb attachment.

The pelvic girdle consists of the os coxae, or hip bone, which is the largest of all the flat bones. There is an articulation with the sacrum dorsally, and ventrally there is the symphysis of the pelvis. The two os coxal bones, together with the sacrum and the first few coccygeal vertebrae, comprise the bony pelvis.

The os coxae consists of three parts: the ilium, the ischium, and the pubis. These three bones form the acetabulum, which is a large cotyloid cavity that articulates with the head of the femur. The ilium is located on the lateral wall of the pelvis. The pubis is on the anterior wall, and the ischium constitutes the posterior part of the ventral wall.

The ilium is the largest component of the three parts of the os coxae. It consists of two surfaces, three borders, and three different angles. The widest part of the bone is referred to as the wing. The lateral angle, or the tuber coxae, forms the basis for the point of the hip. The two surfaces (the gluteal and the pelvic surface) lie in opposite directions. The gluteal surface faces dorsolaterally and caudally; whereas the pelvic surface faces dorsomedially and cranially. The three borders are the anterior, medial, and lateral borders. The medial border forms the greater sciatic notch. The two angles are termed the tuber sacrum and the tuber coxae. The tuber sacrum curves upward and caudally opposite of the first sacral spine. This is the medial angle. The lateral angle, or tuber coxae, forms the point of the hip and is rough on its surface for muscular attachment. The acetabular angle

Dorsal (Bird's Eye) View of the Pelvis

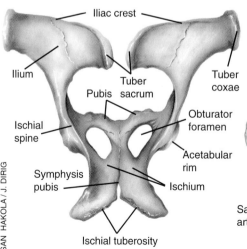

Iliac crest
Ilium
Tuber sacrum
Pubis
Tuber coxae
Ischial spine
Obturator foramen
Symphysis pubis
Acetabular rim
Ischium
Ischial tuberosity

Anterior (Cranial) View

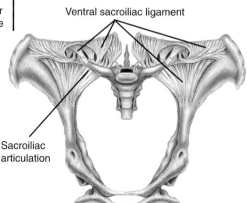

Ventral sacroiliac ligament
Sacroiliac articulation

SUSAN HAKOLA / J. DIRIG

meets the other two bones at the acetabulum, and forms the ischiatic spine on the dorsal border.

The ischium slopes distally and medially and forms the caudal ventral wall of the bony pelvis. This body, or shaft of the ischium, contains two surfaces, four borders, and four different angles. The pelvic and ventral surfaces serve as the hard tissue for the attachment of numerous muscles. The four borders are the anterior, posterior, medial and lateral.

The anterior border forms the posterior boundary of the obturator foramen. The lateral border forms the lesser sciatic notch and the lower boundary of the lesser sciatic foramen. The four angles are as follows: the anterior medial angle, the interior lateral angle, the posterior medial angle, and posterior lateral angle. The anterior medial angle forms the medial boundary of the obturator foramen. The anterior lateral angle bears a portion of the ischiatic spine dorsally. The posterior medial angle joins its opposing structure at the symphysis of the pelvis. The posterior lateral angle forms the tuber ischii to which the biceps femoris and semitendinosus muscles are attached.

the cranial portion of the pelvic floor and contains two surfaces, three borders, and three angles. The pelvic and the ventral surfaces form the two surfaces of the pubis.

Ventral (Belly) View of the Pelvis

1. Origin of rectus femoris
2. Origin of gamellus
3. Origin of biceps femoris
4. Origin of semitendinosus
5. Origin of quadratus femoris
6. Origin of semimembranosus
7. Origin of adductor femoris
8. Origin of gracilis
9. Origin of obturator externus
10. Origin of pectineus

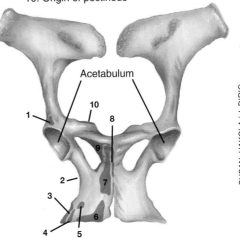

SUSAN HAKOLA / J. DIRIG

The pelvic surface is unique in that it is usually convex in shape in the stallion, but concave in the mare and the horse gelded at a young age. The three borders include the anterior, medial and posterior borders. The posterior border forms the anterior boundary of the obturator foramen, and laterally, contains the obturator groove. The three angles include the medial, the acetabular, and the posterior angle. The acetabular angle joins the ilium and the ischium at the acetabulum. The posterior angle joins the ischium with which it forms the inner boundary of the obturator foramen.

The cotyloid cavity that allows the articulation of the pelvis with the head of the femur is called the

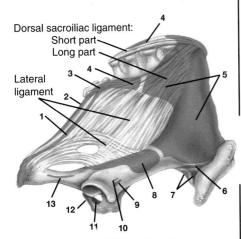

Lateral View of the Pelvis

The os pubis is the smallest of the three bones of the os coxae. It forms

acetabulum. This cavity is directed ventro-laterally, and consists of both an articular and nonarticular portion. The articular portion contains a depression called the acetabular fossa which comprises the nonarticular portion. The acetabular notch contains the transverse, accessory, and round ligaments that travel to the head of the femur.

The oval foramen located between the pubis and ischium is termed the obturator foramen. On the anterior lateral border there is a groove where the obturator nerve and vessels are located.

The entire bony pelvis is formed by the os coxae, the sacrum, and the first three coccygeal vertebrae. Dorsally, the pelvic cavity is formed by the sacrum and first three coccygeal vertebrae. Ventrally, the cavity is formed by the pubic and ischial bones, and laterally, by the ilial and acetabular part of the ischium.

There is a great deal of difference in the size and form of the pelvis between the male and female of the species. The diameter of the pelvic cavity in the mare is much larger than it is in the stallion. The obturator foramina are also larger in the female. The entire cavity is much more spacious in the female, both transversely and when measuring dorsally to ventrally. The ventral surface in the female is also concave, whereas in the stallion, it has more of a convex appearance.

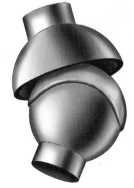

The hip joint is a ball and socket or spheroidal joint with flexion, extension, adduction and abduction motions

The hip joint is a ball and socket joint that is capable of all movements. Flexion and extension have the greatest range of motion within these movements. Abduction, adduction, rotation and circumduction are all possible. It is a very stable joint due to the depth of the acetabulum and its fibrocartilaginous rim that encompasses a great portion of the femoral head. The socket is cut medially by a deep notch that contains the attachment of the round and the accessory ligaments. This notch is called the acetabular notch and fossa.

There are two ligaments that secure the femoral head against luxation. They are the round and the accessory ligaments. The round ligament is attached in the subpubic groove close to the acetabular notch and ends in its attachment within the notch on the head of the femur. The accessory ligament is unique to the equine in that it does not occur in any other domestic species. This ligament extends from the notch on the head of the femur to blend with the prepubic tendon of the abdominal muscle.

Anatomy of the Femur

The femur is the most massive in structure and the largest of the long bones in the horse. It articulates with the acetabulum of the hip proximally, and distally, with tibia and patella. It consists of a shaft and two extremities.

The proximal extremity of the femur includes the head, the neck, and the trochanter major. The head contains the articular surface that corresponds to the acetabulum. This surface is cut medially by a deep notch called the fovea capitis which serves for the attachment of the accessory and round ligaments. The trochanter major serves as the attachment for the deep gluteus and the middle gluteus muscles.

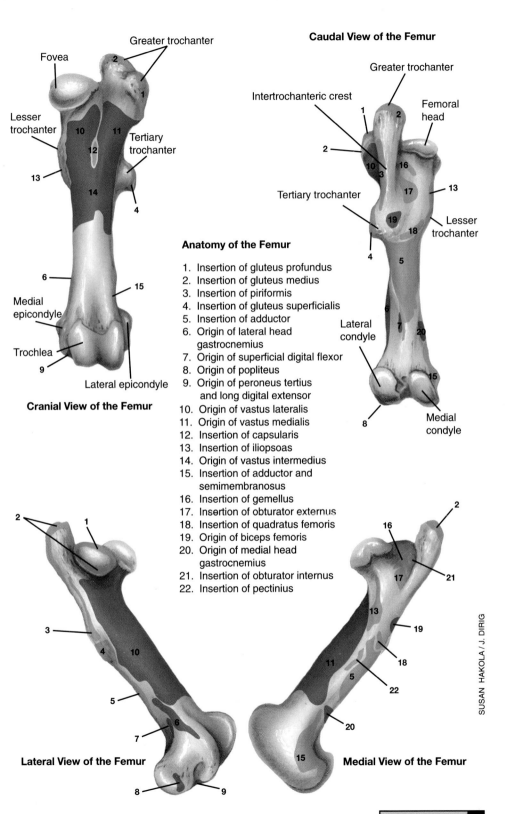

Caudal View of the Femur

Greater trochanter

Fovea

Lesser trochanter

Tertiary trochanter

Intertrochanteric crest

Greater trochanter

Femoral head

Tertiary trochanter

Lesser trochanter

Medial epicondyle

Trochlea

Lateral epicondyle

Cranial View of the Femur

Anatomy of the Femur

1. Insertion of gluteus profundus
2. Insertion of gluteus medius
3. Insertion of piriformis
4. Insertion of gluteus superficialis
5. Insertion of adductor
6. Origin of lateral head gastrocnemius
7. Origin of superficial digital flexor
8. Origin of popliteus
9. Origin of peroneus tertius and long digital extensor
10. Origin of vastus lateralis
11. Origin of vastus medialis
12. Insertion of capsularis
13. Insertion of iliopsoas
14. Origin of vastus intermedius
15. Insertion of adductor and semimembranosus
16. Insertion of gemellus
17. Insertion of obturator externus
18. Insertion of quadratus femoris
19. Origin of biceps femoris
20. Origin of medial head gastrocnemius
21. Insertion of obturator internus
22. Insertion of pectinius

Lateral condyle

Medial condyle

SUSAN HAKOLA / J. DIRIG

Lateral View of the Femur

Medial View of the Femur

Hip & Thigh   61

The distal extremity consists of a trochlea cranially, and two condyles caudally. The trochlea consists of a groove bordered by two separate ridges that form the articular surface for the patella. The medial ridge is much wider and extends higher than the lateral ridge. The two ridges converge distally. The medial and lateral condyles are separated by the intercondyloid fossa and articulate with the condyles of the tibia in forming the stifle joint.

The Sublumbar Musculature of the Pelvis

There are four muscles within this group that basically originate along the bodies or transverse processes of the lumbar vertebrae and the ribs to insert in the pelvic region. Not all of them function to flex the hip, but that is the main action of this group.

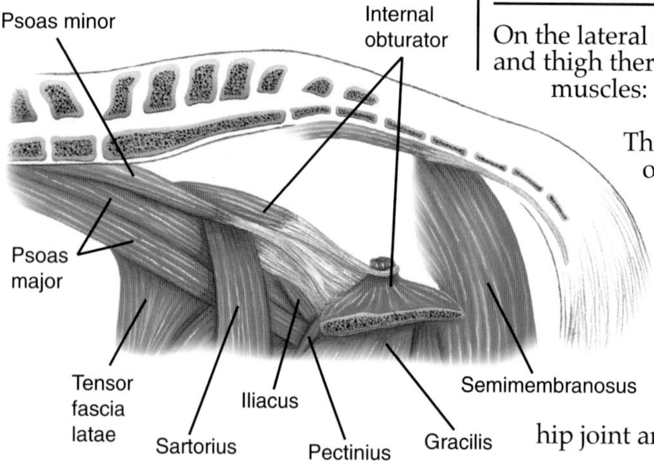

Psoas minor
Internal obturator
Psoas major
Tensor fascia latae
Iliacus
Sartorius
Pectinius
Gracilis
Semimembranosus

Sublumbar Muscles

SUSAN HAKOLA / J. DIRIG

The *psoas minor* originates on the last three thoracic and the first four or five lumbar vertebrae, and inserts on the shaft of the ilium. Its function is to flex the pelvis.

The *psoas major* originates on the transverse process of the lumbar vertebrae and the last two ribs. It inserts on the trochanter minor of

the femur with a common tendon. It functions to flex the hip joint and to rotate the thigh outward.

The *iliacus* is found on the ventral surface of the ilium and lies beneath the medial gluteus. It originates on this ventral surface of the ilium and inserts on the trochanter minor of the femur through a common tendon with the psoas major. Like the psoas major, it also acts to flex the hip joint and rotate the thigh outward.

The *quadratus lumborum* originates on the upper part of the last two ribs and the lumbar transverse processes. It inserts on the wing of the sacrum and communicates with the ventral sacroiliac ligament. It functions to fix the last two ribs and the lumbar vertebrae to produce a lateral flexion.

The Lateral Musculature of the Pelvis and Thigh

On the lateral surface of the pelvis and thigh there are seven distinct muscles:

The *tensor fascia latae* originates from the tuber coxae to insert in a broad aponeurosis upon the patella, the lateral patellar ligament, and the cranial border of the tibia (called the tibial crest.) Its function is to flex the hip joint and extend the stifle.

The muscle beneath and behind the tensor fascia latae is the *gluteus superficialis*. This originates from two areas: the tuber coxae and the gluteal fascia. It inserts on the third trochanter of the femur. This muscle serves to abduct the limb and flex the hip joint.

The very large muscle that lies superficial to the gluteal surface of the ilium and creates the lateral wall of the pelvis is referred to as the *gluteus medius.* This muscle has three different origins. First, it originates from the aponeurosis of the longissimus dorsi. The second origin is from the gluteal surface and tuber of the ilium. The third origin is from the dorsal sacroiliac, the lateral sacroiliac and sacrosciatic ligaments, and the gluteal fascia. Along with the three areas of origin are three different areas of insertion. It inserts on the trochanter major of the femur, the crest below the trochanter, and the lateral aspects of the trochanter ribs. The gluteus medius muscle extends the hip joint and abducts the limb.

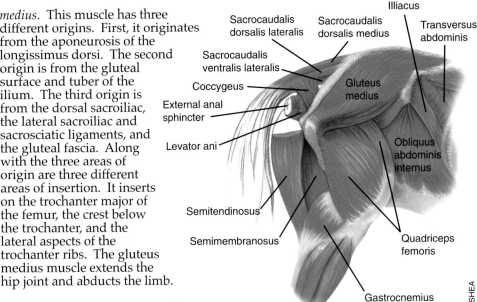

Illiacus

Sacrocaudalis dorsalis lateralis

Sacrocaudalis dorsalis medius

Transversus abdominis

Sacrocaudalis ventralis lateralis

Coccygeus

Gluteus medius

External anal sphincter

Levator ani

Obliquus abdominis internus

Semitendinosus

Semimembranosus

Quadriceps femoris

Gastrocnemius

Deep Lateral View

SUSAN HAKOLA / A. O'SHEA

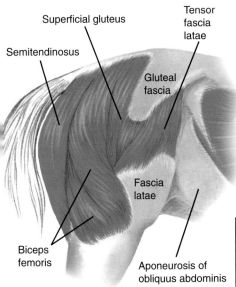

Superficial gluteus

Tensor fascia latae

Semitendinosus

Gluteal fascia

Fascia latae

Biceps femoris

Aponeurosis of obliquus abdominis

Superficial Lateral View

The *biceps femoris* is a large muscle that extends from the sacrum and coccygeal spines to the lateral surfaces of the stifle and leg. Its origins are extensive in that it arises from the dorsal and lateral sacroiliac ligaments, the gluteal and coccygeal facsiae, the intermuscular septum between the biceps femoris and the semitendinosus, and lastly from the tuberosity. It inserts on the posterior surface of the femur, the anterior srface of the patella, and the lateral patellar ligaments. A portion also inserts on the tibial crest and the crural of the tuber calcis. This muscle has a very complex action. The main action is to extend the limb during locomotion; yet it also allows rearing, kicking, and abduction of the limb.

Originating from the superior ischiatic spine and the shaft of the ilium is the *gluteus profundus*. This muscle then inserts on the anterior portion of the trochanter major of the femur. When this muscle contracts, it causes an abduction of the thigh and allows the limb to be rotated inward.

The *semitendinosus* is a long muscle which extends from the transverse processes of the first and second coccygeal vertebrae and the ventral surface of the tuber ichium, to the tibial crest and the crural of the tuber calcis. This muscle functions to extend the hip and hock joints, and also causes a flexion of the stifle, and a rotation of the leg inward.

The *semimembranosus* is a three-sided muscle which originates on the posterior border of the sacrosciatic ligament and the ventral surface of the tuber ischii. It inserts on the medial epicondyle of the femur and functions to extend the hip joint and abduct the limb.

The Medial Musculature of the Pelvis and Thigh

The muscles of the median group of the thigh can can be divided into three layers. The most superficial layer contains the *sartorius* and the *gracilis* muscles. There are three muscles in the middle layer: the *pectineus*, the *adductor* and the *semimembranosus*.

the *sartorius* muscle. This muscle travels distally to insert on the medial patteller ligament and the tuberosity of the tibia. Its main function is to flex the hip and abduct the limb. The sartorius forms the anterior border of the femoral canal in which the femoral artery, vein, and deep inguinal lymph glands are situated.

Caudal to the sartorius is a wide quadrilateral muscle that covers a high percentage of the medial portion of the thigh. This is the *gracilis* muscle. It originates from the pelvic symphysis to the pubic tendon in the accessory ligament. It inserts on the medial patellar ligament, the medial surface of the tibia, and the medial femorotibial ligament. Its sole function is to aid in the adduction of the limb.

Tensor fascia latae, Sartorius, Pectinius, Internal obturator, Gracilis (cut), Rectus femoris, Vastus medialis, Adductor, Gracilis (cut), Semitendinosus, Semimembranosus

SUSAN HAKOLA / J. DIRIG

Superficial and Deep Muscles, Medial View

Lateral to the femur and medial to the gracilis is the *pectineus*. It originates from the prepubic tendon, the accessory ligament, and the anterior border of the pubis. It inserts distally on the medial border of the femur near the nutrient foramen. This muscle has the action of adducting the limb and flexing the hip joint. The femoral canal is formed posteriorly by this muscle.

Originating on the ventral surface of the pubis and the ischium and dividing off from the origin of the gracilis is the *adductor*. This muscle inserts in two places: the posterior surface of the femur along the third trochanter and the medial epicondyle of the femur which includes the medial ligament of the stifle joint. The adductor acts to rotate the femur towards the medial plane, adduct the limb, and extend the hip joint.

The third or deep layer contains four muscles: the *quadratus femoris*, the *obturator externus*, the *obturator internus*, and the *gemellus*.

Originating on the iliac fascia and the tendon of the psoas minor is

Lying beneath the adductor muscle is the *quadratus femoris* which originates on the ventral surface of the ischium just cranial to the semimembranosus. It inserts on the posterior surface of the femur in proximity to the lower portion of the trochanter minor. The action of this muscle is to fold; it extends the hip joint and adducts the thigh.

The *obturator externus* extends from its origination on the ventral surface of the pubis and ischium, around the obturator foramen, to insert on the trochanteric fossa. This muscle acts to adduct the thigh and rotate it outward.

Originating on the pelvic surfaces of the pubis and ischium, the pelvic surface of the shaft of the ilium, and the wing of the sacrum is the *obturator internus*. This muscle travels distally to insert on the trochanter fossa. The action of the obturator internus is to rotate the femur outward.

The last of these small muscles of the hip, the *gemellus*, also acts to rotate the femur outward. It originates along the lateral border of the ischium, near the ischiatic spine and inserts on the trochanteric fossa and ridge. This is a thin triangular muscle that lies deep to the biceps femoris.

The Cranial Musculature of the Pelvis and Thigh

This anterior muscle group is comprised of the *sartorius*, the *quadriceps femoris*, and the *capsularis*.

Covering the cranial and craniolateral surfaces of the femur is the large muscle referred to as the *quadriceps femoris*. It is comprised of four individually named heads of origin, one of which arises from the ilium, while the other three arise from the femur. All four component heads insert onto the patella, and are named as follows:
    1). The *rectus femoris*, which

originates from the shaft of the ilium. It inserts on the base and anterior surface of the patella.
    2). The *vastus lateralis* originates on the lateral border and surface of the femur in the area of the trochanter major. Its insertion is on the lateral part and anterior surface of the patella.
    3). The *vastus medialis*, which originates on the medial surface of the femur to insert on the medial border of the patella. It combines with the proximal portion of the medial patellar ligament.
    4). The *vastus intermedius* originates from the anterior surface of the femur and inserts on the base of the patella and the femoropatellar joint capsule.

All four components of the quadriceps femoris act to extend the stifle joint. The rectus femoris additionally helps in the flexion of the hip joint. The vastus intermedius also helps to raise the femoropatellar capsule during the extension of the stifle joint.

The *iliocapsularis* has its tendinous origin on the ilium and attaches to the proximal third of the anterior surface of the femur. Its sole function may be to raise the joint capsule of the stifle joint during flexion of the joint.

The Neurovascular Supply to the Pelvis and Thigh

The sublumbar musculature is supplied by the intercostal lumbar, the circumflex iliac, and the deep femoral arteries. This muscle group is neurologically supplied by the lumbar nerves with some small branches to the iliacus and psoas major off of the femoral nerve.

The lateral musculature is supplied by the circumflex iliac, iliolumbar, iliofemoral, gluteal, obturator, deep and posterior femoral, and the posterior gluteal arteries. Innervation is supplied by the anterior and posterior gluteal nerves, the main branch of the gluteal , the sciatic, and the peroneal nerves.

The medial muscles of the thigh are supplied by the femoral, the deep femoral and the obturator arteries. Neurologically, the obturator nerve supplies all three components of the second layer. The third layer has vascular origins from the deep femoral obturator and the internal pubic arteries. The obturator externus receives innervation from the obturator nerve. The quadriceps femoris, the obturator internus, and the gemellus all receive innervation from the sciatic nerve.

All of the cranial muscle group receives innervation from the femoral nerve. Blood is supplied to this group by the anterior femoral, the iliofemoral, the femoral, and the popliteal arteries.

U

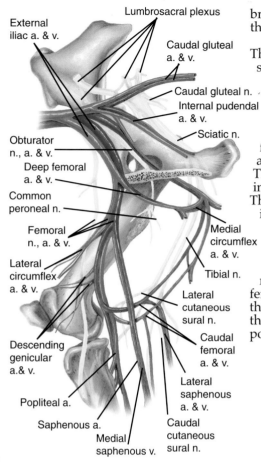

External iliac a. & v.

Lumbrosacral plexus

Caudal gluteal a. & v.

Caudal gluteal n.

Internal pudendal a. & v.

Sciatic n.

Obturator n., a. & v.

Deep femoral a. & v.

Common peroneal n.

Femoral n., a. & v.

Medial circumflex a. & v.

Lateral circumflex a. & v.

Tibial n.

Lateral cutaneous sural n.

Caudal femoral a. & v.

Descending genicular a.& v.

Lateral saphenous a. & v.

Popliteal a.

Saphenous a.

Medial saphenous v.

Caudal cutaneous sural n.

Medial Neurovascular Anatomy

Anatomy of the Stifle Joint

This joint corresponds, anatomically, to the knee joint in man. It is the largest of all joints in the equine and has the most elaborate of all the articulations. It is actually two joints, the femoro-patellar and the femorotibial. Due to the anatomical structure and its location, it is the weakest joint of the horse. The stifle exhibits its own unique areas of distinction such as a locking mechanism. (See the discussion of the locking mechanism found on pages 11 - 12.)

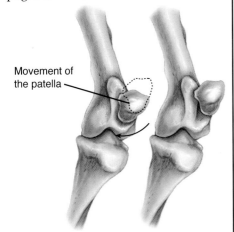

Movement of the patella

Locking Mechanism of the Stifle

The femoropatellar joint is an articulation that is formed between the trochlea of the femur and the articular surfaces of the patella. The joint capsule attaches on the margin of the articular surface of the patella, and on the femur at a distance away from the articular surface. This joint capsule is separated from the quadriceps femorus muscle by a pad of fat. Another fat pad also separates this joint capsule from the patellar ligaments below the patella. Beneath this area, the femoropatellar joint capsule communicates with that of the femorotibial capsules.

There are two femoropatellar ligaments and three patellar ligaments

The two femoropatellar ligaments lie laterally and medially and reinforce the capsule on either side. The lateral arises from the lateral condyle of the femur and inserts on the lateral border of the patella. The medial ligament is not as extensive, and arises above the medial epicondyle of the femur to insert on the patellar fibrocartilage. The lateral patellar ligament extends laterally from the anterior surface of the patella to the two lateral tuberosities of the tibia. This ligament combines with a strong tendon from the biceps femoris muscle and a portion of the fascia latae.

Stifle Joint, Cranial View

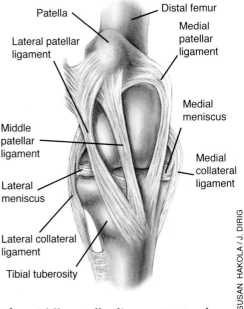

Patella
Lateral patellar ligament
Middle patellar ligament
Lateral meniscus
Lateral collateral ligament
Tibial tuberosity
Distal femur
Medial patellar ligament
Medial meniscus
Medial collateral ligament

SUSAN HAKOLA / J. DIRIG

The middle patellar ligament extends from the apex of the patella to the distal portion of the groove on the tibial tuberosity. Two bursa sacs are located between this ligament and the bone. The first and largest is located in the upper part of the groove and the second smaller one is located between the ligament and the apex of the patella. The medial patellar ligament is the weakest of the three; it attaches above the patellar fibrocartilage and extends to the tibial tuberosity medial to the groove. It is combined with a common aponeurosis from the gracilis and sartorius muscles. The vastus medialis tendoninserts on the proximal portion. The second articulation of the stifle joint is the femorotibial articulation. This is formed between the condyles of the femur and the proximal articular portion of the tibia.

Crescent plates of fibrocartilage, which allow articulation along the articular surfaces of both the femur and tibia, are called menisci. There are lateral and medial menisci, each with a proximal surface that is adapted to the condyle of the femur, and a distal surface which corresponds to the condyle of the tibia.

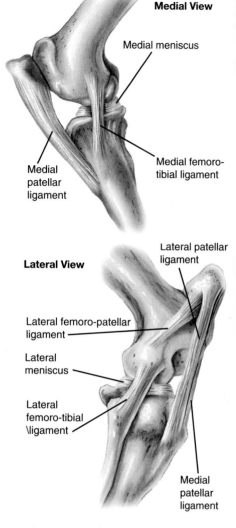

Medial View

Medial meniscus

Medial patellar ligament

Medial femoro-tibial ligament

Caudal View

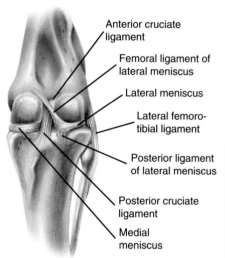

Anterior cruciate ligament

Femoral ligament of lateral meniscus

Lateral meniscus

Lateral femoro-tibial ligament

Posterior ligament of lateral meniscus

Posterior cruciate ligament

Medial meniscus

Lateral View

Lateral patellar ligament

Lateral femoro-patellar ligament

Lateral meniscus

Lateral femoro-tibial \ligament

Medial patellar ligament

There are four ligaments involved with stabilization of the femorotibial articulation of the stifle joint. There are two collateral and two cruciate ligaments. The medial collateral ligament is attached to the medial epicondyle of the femur and extends to the medial condyle of the tibia. The lateral collateral ligament is somewhat thicker. It arises from the upper depression on the lateral epicondyle of the femur and ends on the head of the tibia.

Located in the intercondyloid fossa of the femur, between the synovial sacs, are the two cruciate ligaments. The

anterior cruciate ligament originates from the central fossa on the tibial spine, and extends dorsally and caudally. It inserts on the lateral wall of the intercondyloid fossa. The posterior cruciate ligament is medial to the anterior cruciate ligament and is larger. It is attached to the popliteal notch of the tibia and is directed dorsally and cranially to the anterior portion of the intercondyloid fossa of the femur.

The main movement of the stifle joint is flexion and extension. It has an articular angle of about 150 degrees. The patella moves dorsally upon extension and distally with flexion.

U

Anatomy of the Tibia

Since the fibula is rudimentary, the entire weight of the hind limb is carried on the tibia. It is a long bone which extends distally and caudally from the stifle to the hock joint. Proximally, it articulates with the femur; distally, with the tarsus and laterally, with the fibula.

The proximal end of the tibia is large and three-sided. There are actually two articular eminences present: the medial and lateral condyles. Each of these condyles corresponds to the condyle of the femur and a meniscus for articulation. Centrally, on the proximal end is the intercondyloid eminence. This serves as a division between the two articular condyles.

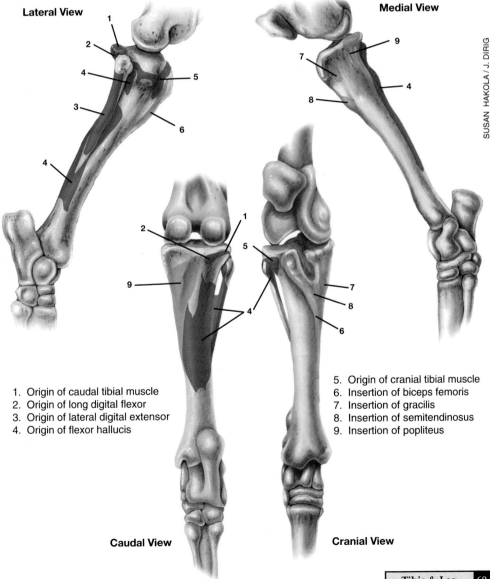

SUSAN HAKOLA / J. DIRIG

Lateral View

Medial View

Caudal View

Cranial View

1. Origin of caudal tibial muscle
2. Origin of long digital flexor
3. Origin of lateral digital extensor
4. Origin of flexor hallucis
5. Origin of cranial tibial muscle
6. Insertion of biceps femoris
7. Insertion of gracilis
8. Insertion of semitendinosus
9. Insertion of popliteus

Posterior to this intercondyloid eminence is the intercondyloid fossa, in which the anterior cruciate ligament is attached. Caudal to these condyles is the deep popliteal notch. The tibial tuberosity is the large anterior eminence of the tibia that is marked in the front by a groove. The distal portion of this groove provides the attachment for the middle patellar ligament. Lateral and medial to this groove, are rough areas for the attachment of the medial and lateral patellar ligaments.

The shaft of the tibia is large and widens at the distal end. The medial surface provides the attachment of the medial ligament, the sartorius, and the gracilis muscles. The lateral surface is smooth and somewhat spiral. The posterior surfaces flatten and are divided into two parts by the popliteal line. This line runs from the proximal portion of the lateral border to the middle of the medial border.

The distal end of the tibia has a much smaller surface area than its proximal counterpart. The articular surface found here coincides to the trochlea of the tibial tarsal bone and consists of two narrow grooves separated by a ridge. The collateral ligaments of the hock joint are attached to malleoli. The medial malleolus is the more prominent of the two. It forms the anterior border boundary of a groove for the tendon of the long digital flexor muscle. The lateral malleolus is broader and is marked by a vertical groove for the passage of the extensor tendon.

The Fibula

The fibula of the equine is rudimentary in development. It has a shaft which is a slender rod forming the lateral boundary of the interosseus space. The fibular termination occurs one-half to two-thirds of the way down the lateral border of the tibia. The proximal end is relatively large and is flattened transversely. The upper border of this proximal end articulates with the lateral condyle of the tibia. The lateral surface is smooth and provides attachment for the lateral ligament of the stifle joint. The distal end fuses with the shaft of the tibia.

Musculature of the Hind Leg

The musculature within this region can be divided into two groups: a dorsolateral group which includes flexors of the hock and extensors of the digit, and a plantar group which includes extensors of the hock and flexors of the digit. The dorsolateral group is composed of the tibialis cranialis, peroneus tertius, and the long and lateral digital extensors. The plantar, or caudal group, is composed of the popliteus, the gastrocnemius, soleus and the superficial and deep digital flexors.

Originating on the extensor fossa of the femur, sharing a common tendon with the peroneus tertius, and inserting on the extensor process of the third phalanx and the dorsal surface of the first and second phalanges, is the *long digital extensor*. This muscle acts to extend the digit and flex the hock. It also aids in fixing the stifle joint during its range of motion. At the level of the midcannon bone(third metatarsal,) it joins with the tendon of the lateral extensor. The long digital extensor is the largest muscle of the dorsolateral group. It is surrounded by a synovial sheath at the level of the midtarsal region and held in place by three retinacula as it travels across the hock.

The *lateral digital extensor* travels between the long extensor and the deep flexor on the lateral side of the limb. It originates from three locations: the lateral ligament of the stifle joint, the fibula, and the lateral border of the tibia. It inserts on the tendon of the long extensor, approximately one-third of the way down the metatarsus. The tendon of this muscle is also held down by retinacula and is protected by a synovial sheath as it crosses the hock.

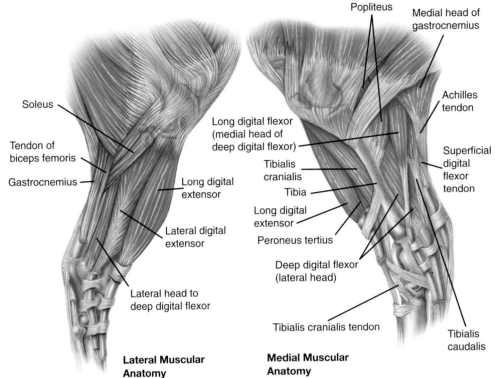

Popliteus

Medial head of gastrocnemius

Achilles tendon

Soleus

Long digital flexor (medial head of deep digital flexor)

Tendon of biceps femoris

Gastrocnemius

Long digital extensor

Tibialis cranialis

Tibia

Long digital extensor

Peroneus tertius

Superficial digital flexor tendon

Lateral digital extensor

Deep digital flexor (lateral head)

Lateral head to deep digital flexor

Tibialis cranialis tendon

Tibialis caudalis

Lateral Muscular Anatomy

Medial Muscular Anatomy

SUSAN HAKOLA / J. DIRIG

The main action of the lateral digital extensor is to assist the long extensor in flexion of the hock, and extension of the digits.

A muscle that is almost entirely composed of tendinous tissue is the *peroneus tertius*. It originates from the extensor fossa of the femur, in the same area as the long digital extensor muscle. At the level of the hock, it bifurcates into a lateral and dorsal branch. The lateral branch has two areas of insertion: the calcaneous and the fourth tarsal bone. The dorsal branch inserts on the proximal part of the third tarsal and third metatarsal bones. When the stifle joint is flexed, the lateral digital extensor muscle acts mechanically to also flex the hock.

The *tibialis cranialis* originates from the lateral condyle and border of the tibia in a small area on the lateral surface of the tuberosity. It inserts on a ridge on the cranial proximal end of the third metatarsal and the first tarsal bones. Its sole action is to flex the hock.

The most superficial and largest muscle of the plantar group is the *gastrocnemius*. This muscle extends from the distal third of the femur where it arises from two heads on the supracondylar tuberosities of the femur. The gastrocnemius extends to the point of the hock where it exchanges position with the superficial flexor tendon before it inserts. The two heads originate, laterally and medially, from the femur. The lateral head originates from the lateral supra-condyloid crest, and the medial head from the medial supracondyloid crest. These heads unite to form a strong, single tendon that is the major component of the calcanean tendon that inserts on the posterior portion of the tuber calcis. The gastrocnemius acts to extend the hock and flex the stifle joint; however, these two functions can not occur simultaneously.

The *soleus* is a very small muscle in the equine. It originates from the head of the fibula and inserts on the tendon of the gastrocnemius at the level of the distal fourth of the leg. Its sole action is to assist the gastrocnemius.

Originating from the supracondylar fossa of the femur beneath the gastrocnemius is the *superficial digital flexor* muscle. It inserts on the tuber calcis and on the medial and lateral eminences of the proximal extremity of the second phalanx and the distal extremity of the first phalanx. This muscle is mostly tendinous, although it has a greater content of muscle tissue than that of the peroneus tertius. As it extends down the leg distally, it forms a cap on the calcanean tuber. A large synovial bursa protects the expanded tendon from the distal fourth of the tibia to the middle of the tarsus. The bursa also extends proximally, between the flexor and gastrocnemius tendons in this area. Because there is little muscle tissue, the superficial digital flexor acts mechanically to flex the digit and extend the hock joint.

There are three heads that originate and later unite in a single tendon that forms the *deep digital flexor* muscle. The three heads of origin are as follows:
   1). The posterior edge of the lateral condyle of the tibia.
   2). The border of the lateral condyle of the tibia just caudal to the facet for the fibula.
   3). The middle third of the posterior surface and the proximal portion of the lateral border of the tibia. This head also originates from the posterior border of the fibula and the interosseous ligament.

These three heads travel distally, to form a single tendon of insertion upon the semilunar crest of the third phalanx. This muscle acts to flex the digit and extend the hock joint. The medial head is termed the long digital flexor. As it travels distally over the hock, it is enclosed within a synovial sheath that extends from the distal fourth of the tibia to its junction with

the common tendon approximately one-third of the way down the metatarsus. The superficial head of the deep digital flexor is called the tibialis posterior. It has a flattened belly and terminates in the distal third of the tibia on a flat tendon which soon fuses with this muscle. The deep head is the largest of the three heads. It lies on the posterior surface of the tibia and contains a great deal of tendinous tissue. The check ligament combines with this tendon at the level just distal to the hock. It is longer in the hind limb than that in the forelimb, but is much weaker and sometimes absent. A tarsal sheath encloses this tendon about the level of the medial malleolus distally, to approximately one-fourth of the way down the metatarsus.

The *popliteus* is a thick triangular muscle that lies on the posterior surface of the tibia. It originates on the lateral epicondyle of the femur and inserts on the caudal medial border of the tibia. This muscle acts to flex the stifle and help to rotate the leg inward.

Neurovascular Supply to the Muscles of the Hind Limb

The entire dorsolateral group is supplied by the anterior tibial artery and its branches. The peroneal nerve also innervates the long digital extensor, the lateral digital extensor, the peroneus tertius and the tibialis anterior.

All five muscles of the plantar group are innervated by the tibial nerve and its corresponding branches. The posterior tibial artery provides the blood supply to the soleus, the popliteus, and the deep digital flexor muscles. The posterior femoral artery supplies the superficial digital flexor muscle. The popliteal artery supplies the popliteus muscle and the gastrocnemius muscle.
U

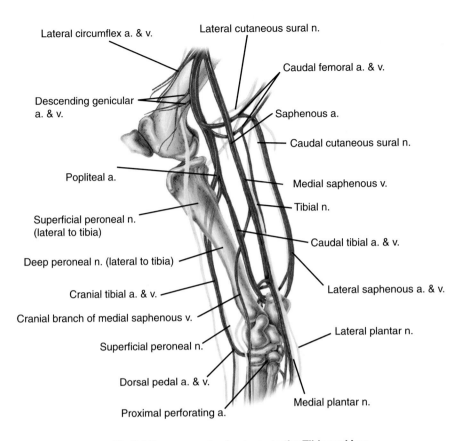

Lateral circumflex a. & v.

Lateral cutaneous sural n.

Caudal femoral a. & v.

Descending genicular a. & v.

Saphenous a.

Caudal cutaneous sural n.

Popliteal a.

Medial saphenous v.

Tibial n.

Superficial peroneal n. (lateral to tibia)

Caudal tibial a. & v.

Deep peroneal n. (lateral to tibia)

Cranial tibial a. & v.

Lateral saphenous a. & v.

Cranial branch of medial saphenous v.

Lateral plantar n.

Superficial peroneal n.

Dorsal pedal a. & v.

Medial plantar n.

Proximal perforating a.

SUSAN HAKOLA / J. DIRIG

Medial Neurovascular Anatomy to the Tibia and Leg

The Bones of the Hock

The hock, or tarsus, is comprised of three rows of bones called the tarsal bones. The talus and calcaneus comprise the proximal row. A central tarsal bone is the main component of the intermediate row, along with portions of the fused first and second tarsal bones. The third and fourth tarsal bones, in addition to the fused first and second tarsals, form the distal row of the hock.

The talus, or tibial tarsal bone, is the medial component of the proximal row. Its distinctive trochlea consists of two oblique ridges that articulate and coincide with the distal end of the tibia. The distal surface articulates with the central tarsal bone. The plantar surface is extremely irregular and possesses four facets for articulation with the fibular tarsal bone, or calcaneus.

The fibular tarsal bone, or calcaneus, is the largest bone of the hock. The tuber calcis, or point of the hock, is formed at its proximal end. The tendon of the gastrocnemius is attached posteriorly on this eminence. The tendons of the superficial digital flexor, biceps femoris, and semitendinosus muscles insert on the cranial portion of this eminence. Distally, the calcaneus articulates with the fourth tarsal bone. The sustentaculum tali, a distinct process, projects inward on the medial surface. The deep flexor tendon travels through a groove along the plantar surface. Dorsally, there are articulations with the talus.

The middle row of the hock is formed by the central tarsal bone. It is situated between the talus and the third tarsal. Proximally, it articulates with the talus, and distally with the

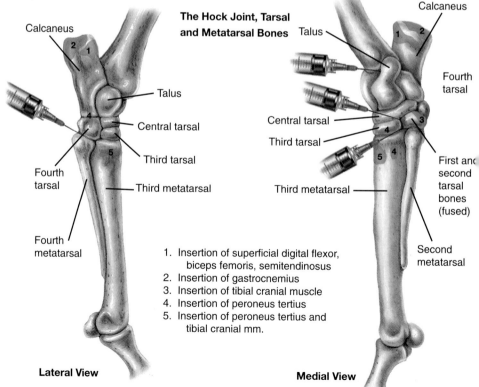

The Hock Joint, Tarsal and Metatarsal Bones

Calcaneus

Talus

Fourth tarsal

Central tarsal

Third tarsal

First and second tarsal bones (fused)

Second metatarsal

Third metatarsal

Calcaneus

Talus

Central tarsal

Third tarsal

Third metatarsal

Fourth tarsal

Fourth metatarsal

1. Insertion of superficial digital flexor, biceps femoris, semitendinosus
2. Insertion of gastrocnemius
3. Insertion of tibial cranial muscle
4. Insertion of peroneus tertius
5. Insertion of peroneus tertius and tibial cranial mm.

Lateral View

Medial View

SUSAN HAKOLA / J. DIRIG

third and the fused first and second tarsals. The lateral border articulates with the fourth tarsal.

The distal row of tarsal bones is composed of the fused first and second tarsal bone, the third and the fourth tarsal bones. The first and second tarsal bones compose the medial plantar portion of the distal row, distal to the central tarsal and caudal to the third tarsal bone.

Located between the central tarsal dorsally, and the metatarsal bone distally, is the third tarsal bone. It articulates distally with the third metatarsal bone, medially with the second tarsal, and laterally with the fourth tarsal.

The lateral portion of the distal row of the tarsal bones contains the fourth tarsal bone. Proximally, it articulates with the fibular tarsal, or calcaneus. Distally, it rests on the third metatarsal and lateral fourth metatarsal. The fourth tarsal articulates medially with the third tarsal bone.

The Metatarsal Bones

The three metatarsal bones have the same general anatomy as their corresponding metacarpal bones. However, there are several important differences. The metatarsals are aligned on the hind limb and are slightly oblique.

The third metatarsal is approximately one-sixth longer than its corresponding metacarpal. This translates to a difference of about two inches in length in a medium sized animal. In cross section, the shaft of the metatarsal is more cylindrical than that of its corresponding metacarpal.

The small second and fourth metatarsal bones are slightly longer than the corresponding second and fourth metacarpals. The fourth, or lateral metatarsal bone, is relatively massive in its proximal portion. Overall, it is larger than the medial, or second, metatarsal bone.

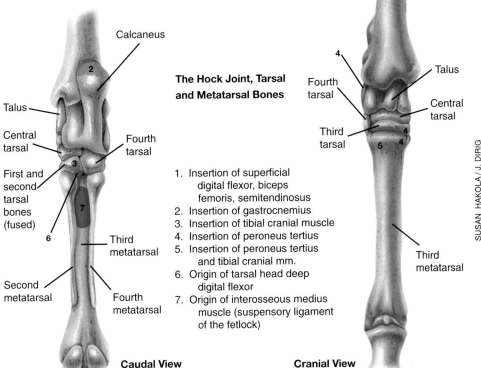

Calcaneus

Talos

Central tarsal

First and second tarsal bones (fused)

Second metatarsal

Fourth tarsal

Third metatarsal

Fourth metatarsal

The Hock Joint, Tarsal and Metatarsal Bones

Fourth tarsal

Third tarsal

Talus

Central tarsal

Third metatarsal

1. Insertion of superficial digital flexor, biceps femoris, semitendinosus
2. Insertion of gastrocnemius
3. Insertion of tibial cranial muscle
4. Insertion of peroneus tertius
5. Insertion of peroneus tertius and tibial cranial mm.
6. Origin of tarsal head deep digital flexor
7. Origin of interosseous medius muscle (suspensory ligament of the fetlock)

SUSAN HAKOLA / J. DIRIG

Caudal View

Cranial View

The Hock Joint

The hock joint of the equine is actually a joint composed of a number of articulations. These articulations can generally be divided into:
1). The tarsocrural articulation
2). The intertarsal articulation
3). The tarsometatarsal articulation

The tarsocrural joint is a typical ginglymus joint that is formed by the articulation of the trochlea of the tibial tarsal bone and the corresponding articular surface of the distal end of the tibia. The articular surface on the trochlea of the talus covers almost twice the surface area as that of the corresponding articular surface on the distal end of the tibia. There are ridges and grooves on this trochlear surface that are directed at an angle of twelve to fifteen degrees dorsolateral to the limb's sagittal plane.

The intertarsal and the tarsometatarsal joints within the hock are capable of only a small range-of-motion. These joints are plane joints, and can move only by a gliding movement.

The joint capsule extends from the margin of the tibial articular surface to the metatarsal surfaces distally. It is attached to the surfaces of bones and blends with the collateral ligaments.

To facilitate intraarticular administration of medication, it is important to know the location of the four synovial sacs found within the hock joint. These are as follows:
1). The tibiotarsal sac which lubricates the proximal joint. It is the largest of the four sacs.
2). The proximal intertarsal sac which lines the joints formed by the tibial and fibular tarsal bones above and the central and fourth tarsal bones below. This sac communicates cranially with the tibiotarsal sac.
3). The distal intertarsal sac provides a pouch for lubrication of the joints between the central tarsal bone and bones below, and on either side.
4). The tarsal metatarsal sac lubricates the joints formed by the tarsal and metatarsal bones, the joints between the proximal ends of the metatarsal bone and those joints of the third tarsal bones, and with the bones on either side.

The Ligamentous Structures of the Hock

There are six common ligaments of the hock joint. On the lateral side, there is the long lateral ligament and the short lateral ligament. Medially, there are the long and short medial ligaments. On the plantar surface, there is a plantar ligament, and on the dorsal surface, a dorsal ligament is found.

The long lateral ligament is superficial. It arises on the posterior portion on the lateral malleolus. It travels distally to attach to the fibular and fourth tarsal bone, and the large and lateral small metatarsal bones. The lateral extensor tendon passes through a canal formed by this ligament. The short lateral ligament rises on the anterior part of the lateral malleolus, and travels caudally to end on the lateral surface of the tibial tarsal and the fibular tarsal bones.

The long medial ligament is also superficial. It arises on the posterior portion of the medial malleolus and attaches to the distal tuberosity of the tibial tarsal, and the large and medial small metatarsal bones. The short medial ligament lies beneath the long medial ligament. It arises on the medial malleolus and travels caudally and distally to divide into two branches. One of these ends on the proximal tuberosity of the medial surface of the tibial tarsal bone. The other one terminates on the sustenaculum tali.

The plantar ligament covers the lateral part of the plantar surface of the tarsus. It attaches to the plantar surface of the fibular and fourth tarsal bones, and the proximal end of the lateral metatarsal bone. The dorsal ligament arises from the distal

of the lateral metatarsal bone. The dorsal ligament arises from the distal tuberosity on the medial facet of the tibial tarsl bone. It travels to the central and third tarsal bones and to the proximal ends of the large and small medial metatarsal bones.

The Hock Articulation

The hock joint is flexed through a contraction of the tibialis cranialis muscle and the passive pull of the tendinous peroneus tertius muscle. Extension of the joint is accomplished through contraction of the gastrocnemius, the biceps femoris, and the semitendinosus muscles, and through the passive pull of the tendinous superficial digital flexor muscles. When the horse is in a standing position, the articular angle, measured on the dorsal surface, is about 150 degrees. Complete extension is prevented through

the stabilization of the collateral ligaments.

Flexion is restricted by contact with the metatarsus of the leg, provided the stifle joint is also flexed. The long collateral ligaments are tensed in extension, and the short ones are tensed in flexion of the hock joint. All movements within the hock joint must correspond with those of the stifle. This is because of the tendinous bands, dorsally and caudally, which extend from the upward part of the femur to the tarsus and metatarsus.

The inferior check ligament of the deep digital flexor arises from the plantar aspect of the fibrous joint capsule of the hock. This ligament is much weaker in structure than the corresponding inferior check ligament of the forelimb and may even be absent in the hind limb.

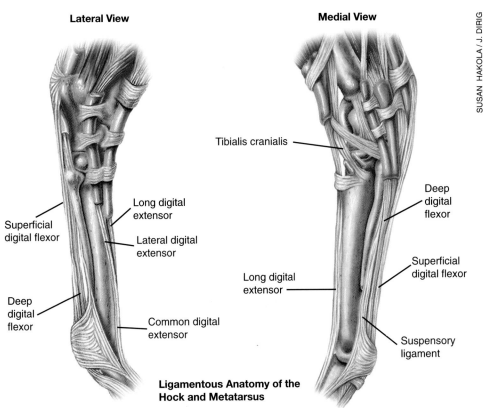

Lateral View

Medial View

SUSAN HAKOLA / J. DIRIG

Tibialis cranialis

Superficial digital flexor

Long digital extensor

Lateral digital extensor

Deep digital flexor

Common digital extensor

Deep digital flexor

Long digital extensor

Superficial digital flexor

Suspensory ligament

Ligamentous Anatomy of the Hock and Metatarsus

The Neurovascular Supply

The superficial peroneal nerve has two terminal branches that descend distally on the dorsal and lateral surfaces of the metatarsus. The caudal cutaneous sural nerve descends distally from the lateral aspect of the hock over the dorsolateral portion of the third metatarsal bone to terminate within the cutaneous structures of the fetlock. This saphenous nerve supplies the medial skin of the metatarsus to the fetlock.

On the lateral and medial aspects of the metatarsus, the lateral and medial plantar nerves lie plantar to their satellite veins and arteries, along the lateral or medial border of the deep digital flexor tendon. These plantar nerves innervate the lateral, medial, and plantar structures of the metatarsus. Between the two flexor tendons, the lateral plantar nerve emerges to reach the lateral borders. From this location, a deep branch arises which is the parent trunk the deeply located lateral and medial plantar metatarsal nerves. These nerves correspond to the same courses as that of the palmar metacarpal nerves of the forelimb. In the area of the midmetatarsus, the medial plantar nerve gives off communicating branches that angle laterally and distally across the superficial digital flexor tendon. It joins the lateral plantar nerve in the area of the distal fourth of the metatarsus.

In the area of the proximal metatarsus, the medial and lateral plantar vessels give rise to the deep plantar arterial and venous arches. It is from these arches that the medial and lateral plantar metatarsal vessels originate.

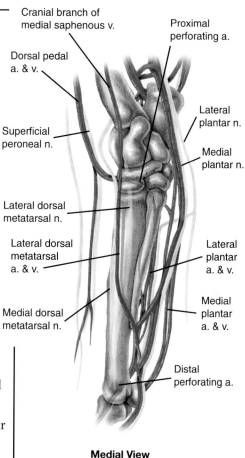

Medial View

Traveling obliquely across the medial surface of the cannon bone is the dorsal common digital vein. At the level of the distal third of the metatarsus, the dorsal common digital vein joins the medial plantar vein just before the medial plantar vein becomes the medial digital vein at the fetlock. The distal deep plantar arch is formed by an anastomosis of the medial plantar vein to the lateral plantar vein.

∪

Anatomical Differences of the Fetlock, Pastern and Digit of the Hindlimb Versus the Forelimb

The first phalanx of the hindlimb is slightly shorter, wider above and narrower below, than its corresponding counterpart of the forelimb. The second phalanx, or middle phalanx, is narrower and longer in the hindlimb than it is in the forelimb. The third phalanx is also narrower. The angle of inclination of the dorsal surface is greater, than that of the forelimb. When an axis through these hindlimb phalanges is drawn with one of the ground plane, the angle is about five degrees greater in the hindlimb than it is in the forelimb. This is caused by the differences in shape, size, and bones of the phalanges. The proximal sesamoids are slightly smaller, and the distal sesamoid is shorter and narrower than those found in the forelimb.

The tendon of the lateral digital extensor does not attach to the proximal phalanx, as it does in the thoracic limb. The suspensory apparatus and the digital flexor tendons are very similar to those of the forelimb. The articular angle of the fetlock is about five degrees greater in the hindlimb than in the forelimb.

The inferior check ligament of the deep digital flexor arises from the plantar aspect of the fibrous joint capsule of the hock. This ligament is much weaker in structure than its corresponding forelimb structure, and may even be absent in the hind limb.

There are several significant differences between the hindfoot and the forefoot. The angle of the toe of the hindfoot is slightly greater and usually ranges from fifty to sixty-two degrees. The hindfoot is narrower in shape than the forefoot. On the distal phalanx, the plantar surface is more concave when compared to the plantar surface of the forefoot. The hindlimb plantar processes are closer together and are not as well developed.

At the area of the proximal metatarsus, the medial and lateral plantar vessels give rise to the deep plantar arterial and venous arches. It is from these arches that the medial and lateral plantar metatarsal vessels originate. As they travel distally, in the area of the fetlock joint, these medial and lateral plantar metatarsal vessels join the medial and lateral digital vessels that result from the bifurcation of the dorsal metatarsal artery. The dorsal pedal artery is a continuation of the dorsal metatarsal artery. In summary, the cranial tibial, the dorsal pedal, the dorsal and the metatarsal arteries provide the principal blood supply to the hind digit.

Traveling across the medial surface of the cannon bone in an oblique manner, is the dorsal common digital vein. At the level of the distal third of the metatarsus, the dorsal common digital vein joins the medial plantar vein just before this becomes the medial digital vein at the fetlock. The distal deep plantar arch is formed by an anastomosis of the medial plantar vein to the lateral plantar vein.

The proximal and middle phalanges are supplied by dorsal and plantar branches of the lateral and medial digital arteries as they descend distally on the respective sides of the digit. There is an anastomosis formed with their counterparts from the opposite sides, and in doing so, there is a formation of an arterial circle around each bone. When the lateral and medial digital arteries reach the distal phalanx, they send a dorsal branch through the foramen, the plantar process, and onto the parietal surface of the bone. The digital arteries continue to the sole surface of the third phalanx where they enter the respective sole foramen, forming an internal arch in an anastamosis within the bone.

There is a dense venous plexus in the coronary and laminar dermis, and in the dermis of the sole. This venous plexus drains into the medial and lateral digital veins. The digital veins accompany the arteries in this region, although not all arterial branches are accompanied by corresponding veins.

The medial and lateral plantar metatarsal nerves supply the fetlock and give rise to the medial and lateral digital nerves.
U

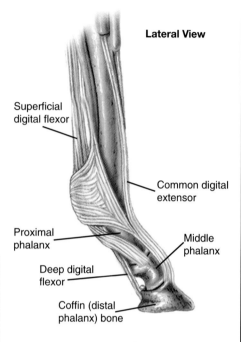

Lateral View

Superficial digital flexor

Common digital extensor

Proximal phalanx

Middle phalanx

Deep digital flexor

Coffin (distal phalanx) bone

SUSAN HAKOLA / J. DIRIG

Medial View

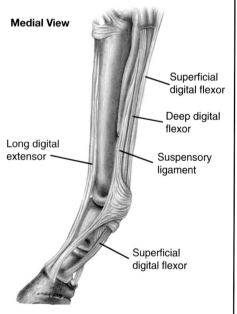

Superficial digital flexor

Deep digital flexor

Long digital extensor

Suspensory ligament

Superficial digital flexor

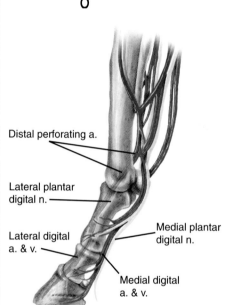

Distal perforating a.

Lateral plantar digital n.

Lateral digital a. & v.

Medial plantar digital n.

Medial digital a. & v.

Medial View of the Neurovascular Anatomy of the Hindlimb Digit

The vertebral column is a critical and fundamental part of the equine skeleton. It may be divided into five different regions: the cervical, the thoracic, the lumbar, the sacral, and the coccygeal. This column extends as a chain of unpaired medium bones from the skull to the end of the tail. Several of these vertebrae are fused or fixed vertebrae, while the others are movable and articulate with each other. Seven cervical, eighteen thoracic, six lumbar, five sacral, and approximately twenty coccygeal vertebrae comprise the vertebral column. The number of coccygeal vertebrae varies between sixteen and twenty-one.

The Cervical Vertebrae

There are seven cervical vertebrae. The first and second cervical vertebrae differ in conformation to the remaining five in that they function to support and move the head.

The atlas is the first cervical vertebra. Its structure differs greatly from that of the other vertebrae in the cervical region. It has

Atlas (C-1)

two wings which project laterally, and forms a ring of bone. Within this ring, or vertebral foramen, two lateral masses are connected by dorsal and ventral arches. Ventrally, the dorsal arch is concave and has a medial dorsal tubercle. On either side, near the anterior border, are the intervertebral foramen. The anterior border is notched and the posterior border is thin and concave. The ventral arch is thicker, narrower and less curved in structure than the dorsal arch. On the lower surface of this ventral arch is the ventral tubercle. This is where the terminal tendon of the longus colli muscle is inserted. The upper face of the ventral arch has an articular surface called the fovea dentis on which the dens of the axis rests.

The second cervical vertebra, the axis, is the longest of the vertebrae. It is characterized by a projection from the anterior portion of the body called the dens. The body of the axis has an anterior extremity called the dens which contains a convex articular ventral surface for articulation with the ventral arch of

Axis (C-2)

SUSAN HAKOLA / A. O'SHEA

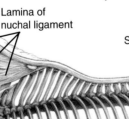

Lamina of nuchal ligament

Supraspinous ligament

The Vertebral Column

| 7 Cervical | 18 Thoracic | 6 Lumbar | 5 Sacral | 16-21 Caudal |

contain articular surfaces confluent ventrally with the dens. The ventral branch of the second cervical nerve communicates through a foramen that is present in the arch along the anterior border. The nerve traverses downward and backward along this grooved foramen. The spinous process is very prominent with the lateral surfaces being concave and rough for muscular attachment.

The third, fourth and fifth cervical vertebrae decrease in length from the third to the last. The bodies of these vertebrae are long when compared to other types of vertebrae. The ventral surface contains a ventral spine. The anterior articular processes are directed dorsomedially. The posterior articular processes are located ventrolaterally. Transverse processes are large, plate-like and occur both medially and laterally.

The sixth cervical vertebra is shorter and wider than the fifth. Articular processes are shorter and further apart. The spinous processes are rudimentary. Transverse processes have three branches, the third of which is thick and almost a sagittal plate.

The seventh cervical vertebra is the shortest, and is wider than all the others. The body is flattened dorsoventrally. There is a facet on each side for articulation with part of the head of the first rib. The anterior articular processes are wider and longer than the posterior pair. The spinous process is now more than an inch or so in height.

The Thoracic Vertebrae

There are eighteen thoracic vertebrae in the horse. These vertebrae contain surfaces that articulate with the ribs and have very noticeable spinous processes. The bodies of these vertebrae are short and constrict in the middle. The corresponding ends are wider. The anterior surfaces are convex and the posterior surfaces are concave. Anterior and posterior

costal facets of each vertebra, along with those of adjacent vertebrae, form sockets for the heads of the ribs. Articular processes are small and are presented by only two oval facets on the anterior part of the arch. The processes face almost directly dorsally. Posterior processes arise from the base of the spinous processes. Their facet faces are directed ventrally.

Thoracic Vertebra

The Lumbar Vertebrae

There are six lumbar vertebrae in the equine. Instead of the conspicuous spinous processes of the thoracic vertebrae, the lumbar vertebrae are noted by their characteristic transverse processes. The anterior surface has a dorsally oriented concave surface for articulation with the posterior pair of processes for the preceding vertebra. This forms the anterior articular process. The posterior articular process projects from the arch of the base of the spinous process and has a ventrally convex articular surface. Transverse processes are elongated plates, flattened dorsoventrally, which project outward and may incline slightly upward or downward. The longest transverse process occurs at the level of the third and fourth lumbar vertebrae. Their length then decreases to the sixth. The last lumbar vertebra contains an articular surface along the transverse process for articulation with the wing of the sacrum.

Lumbar Vertebra

Sacrum

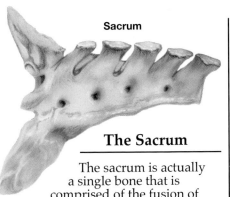

The Sacrum

The sacrum is actually a single bone that is comprised of the fusion of five vertebrae. Triangular in shape, it articulates on each side with the ilium. Dorsally, there are five sacral spines which are directed dorsally and caudally. There are four dorsal sacrum foramina from which the dorsal branches of the sacral nerves emerge. The pelvic surface is concave in length, wide in front, and narrow behind. A ventral sacral foramen is present which allows passage of the ventral divisions of the sacral nerves.

The Coccygeal Vertebrae

Coccygeal vertebrae usually average approximately eighteen in number. From the first to the last, they become reduced in size and consist mainly of a structural body. The spinous processes decrease from the first to the last, as do the transverse processes. Actual articular processes are not present, but rudiments of the anterior articular processes commonly occur. The last coccygeal vertebra has a pointed end.

The Cervical Musculature

The dorsal surfaces of the cervical vertebrae contain the nuchal ligament. This ligament divides the dorsal cervical muscles into right and left groups. It supports much of the burden of the head and allows the head to be raised and lowered. The

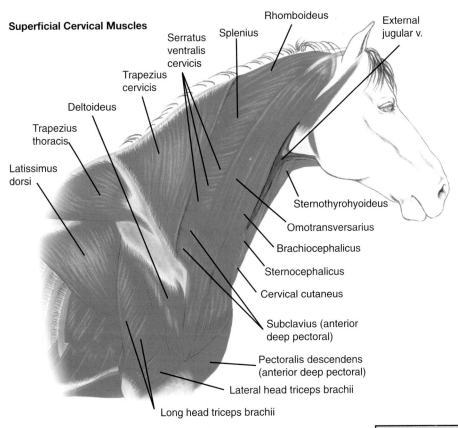

Superficial Cervical Muscles

Rhomboideus

External jugular v.

Serratus ventralis cervicis

Splenius

Trapezius cervicis

Deltoideus

Trapezius thoracis

Latissimus dorsi

Sternothyrohyoideus

Omotransversarius

Brachiocephalicus

Sternocephalicus

Cervical cutaneus

Subclavius (anterior deep pectoral)

Pectoralis descendens (anterior deep pectoral)

Lateral head triceps brachii

Long head triceps brachii

SUSAN HAKOLA / A. O'SHEA

nuchal ligament has two distinct parts. The dorsal part is a thick cord that extends between the highest spines of the withers and the external occipital protuberance of the skull. Extending from the withers, it becomes the narrow supraspinous ligament. The second portion forms a sheath closely applied to the first portion. It consists of bundles of elastic fibers that run cranioventrally from the spines of the first, second, and third thoracic vertebrae, to attach to the second through the seventh cervical vertebrae. Synovial bursae are located between the two portions of the nuchal ligament and certain bony structures to minimize friction. The nuchal bursa is present above the dorsal arch of the atlas. There is a second bursa found along the spine of the axis. A third, the supraspinous bursa, is located over most of the spinous process of the thoracic vertebrae located at the withers.

There are twelve pairs of muscles that lie ventrally and laterally to the cervical vertebrae. They are:
1). The *cutaneus colli* is located on the ventral region of the neck arising from the cariniform cartilage to attach to the cervical fascia.
2). The *brachiocephalicus* originates along the wing of the atlas and the transverse processes of the second, third, and fourth cervical vertebrae to insert on the humerus.
3). The *sternocephalicus* originates from the cariniform cartilage of the sternum to insert on the posterior border of the mandible.
4). The *sternothyroideus* and *sternohyoideus*, which is a digastric muscle, originate on the cartilage of

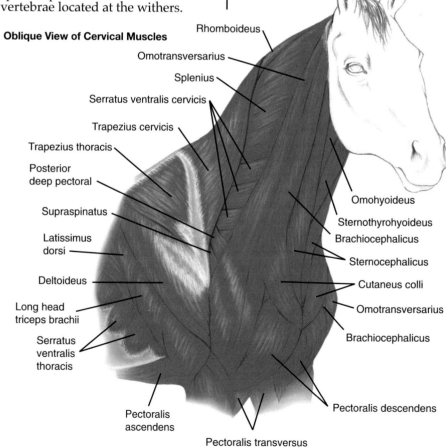

Oblique View of Cervical Muscles

Rhomboideus
Omotransversarius
Splenius
Serratus ventralis cervicis
Trapezius cervicis
Trapezius thoracis
Posterior deep pectoral
Supraspinatus
Latissimus dorsi
Deltoideus
Long head triceps brachii
Serratus ventralis thoracis
Pectoralis ascendens
Pectoralis transversus

Omohyoideus
Sternothyrohyoideus
Brachiocephalicus
Sternocephalicus
Cutaneus colli
Omotransversarius
Brachiocephalicus
Pectoralis descendens

SUSAN HAKOLA/A. O'SHEA

the sternum to insert on the posterior border of the lamina of the thyroid cartilage of the larynx and the body of the hyoid bone, respectively.

5). The *omohyoideus* originates in the subscapular fascia of the shoulder joint to insert on the hyoid bone.

6). The *scalenus* originates on the anterior border and lateral surface of the first rib and inserts on the transverse process of the seventh cervical vertebra and the transverse processes of the sixth, fifth and fourth cervical vertebrae on the ventral surface.

7). The *cervicalis ascendens* muscle is attached to the transverse process of the last three or four cervical vertebrae and the first rib.

8). The *rectus capitis ventralis major* originates on the transverse processes of the fifth, fourth and third cervical vertebrae to insert on the occipital bone.

9). The *rectus capitis ventralis minor* originates on the ventral arch of the atlas to insert on the basilar part of the occipital bone.

10). The *rectus capitis lateralis* originates on the atlas and inserts on the paramastoid process of the occipital bone.

11). The *longus colli* originates on the bodies of the first five or six thoracic vertebrae and the transverse processes of the cervical vertebrae. It inserts on the transverse processes of the last two cervical vertebrae, the bodies of the cervical vertebrae, and ventral tubercle of the atlas.

12). The *intertransversalis colli* muscle occupies the spaces between the lateral aspects of the vertebrae and the transverse and articular processes.

The Lateral Cervical Muscles

This musculature exists as twelve pairs of muscles that are arranged in five different layers. The first layer consists of only one muscle, the *trapezius cervicalis*. This muscle originates on the nuchal ligament from the second cervical to the third thoracic vertebrae.

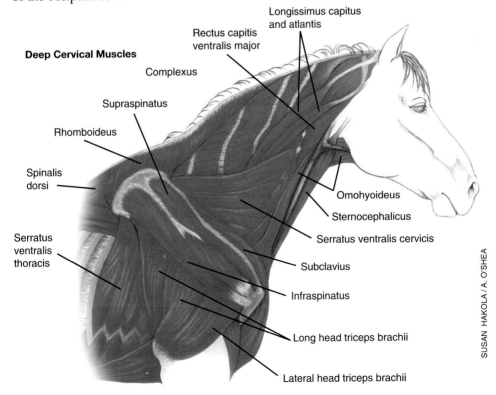

Deep Cervical Muscles

Longissimus capitus and atlantis

Rectus capitis ventralis major

Complexus

Supraspinatus

Rhomboideus

Spinalis dorsi

Serratus ventralis thoracis

Omohyoideus

Sternocephalicus

Serratus ventralis cervicis

Subclavius

Infraspinatus

Long head triceps brachii

Lateral head triceps brachii

SUSAN HAKOLA / A. O'SHEA

It then travels distally to insert on the spine of the scapula.

The second layer consists of the *rhomboideus cervicalis* and the *serratus cervicis* muscles. The rhomboideus cervicalis originates on the nuchal ligament from the second cervical to the second thoracic vertebrae and inserts on the medial surface of the cartilage of the scapula. The serratus cervicis originates from the transverse processes of the last four or five cervical vertebrae to insert on the costal surface of the scapula.

The third layer consists of only one muscle, the *splenius*. This muscle originates from the third, fourth, and fifth thoracic spines through the dorsal scapular ligament and the nuchal ligament. The splenius inserts on the nuchal crest, the mastoid process, and the wing of the atlas, in addition to the transverse processes of the third, fourth and fifth cervical vertebrae.

The fourth layer consists of eight pairs of muscles. The *longissimus capitis* originates on the transverse processes of the first two thoracic vertebrae and the articular processes of the cervical vertebrae. It inserts on the mastoid process and the wing of the atlas.

The *semispinalis capitis* originates on the third, fourth, and fifth thoracic spines by means of the dorsal scapular ligament, transverse processes of the first six or seven thoracic vertebrae, and the articular processes of the cervical vertebrae. It inserts on the rough area of the occipital bone, just ventral to the nuchal crest.

The *multifidus cervicis* muscle originates on the articular processes of the last four or five cervical and the first thoracic vertebrae. It inserts on the spinous and articular processes of the cervical vertebrae.

The *spinalis* muscle is considered a component of the longissimus dorsi muscle.

The *obliquus capitis posterior* muscle originates on the side of the spine and the posterior articular process of the axis. It inserts on the dorsal surface of the wing of the atlas.

The *obliquus capitis anterior* originates on the anterior edge of the ventral surface of the wing of the atlas and inserts on the perimastoid process and nuchal crest of the occipital bone.

The *rectus capitis dorsalis major* muscle originates on the spinous process of the axis. Its insertion is on the occipital bone.

The *rectus capitis dorsalis minor* muscle originates on the dorsal surface of the atlas. It inserts on the occipital bone beneath the preceding muscle, lateral to the nuchal ligament.

Musculature of the Thoracolumbar Spine

There are nine pairs of muscles within this region, arranged in four different layers.

The first layer consists of the *trapezius thoracalis* and the *latissimus dorsi* muscles. The latissimus dorsi originates on the lumbar dorsal fascia along the lumbar and thoracic spines. It inserts on the teres tuberosity of the humerus as far forward as the highest point of the withers. The trapezius thoracalis originates from the superspinous ligament from the third to the tenth thoracic vertebrae. It then travels to insert on the tuber spinae of the scapula.

The second layer consists of the *rhomboideus thoracalis*, the *serratus dorsalis anterior*, and the *serratus dorsalis posterior* muscles. The rhomboideus thoracalis originates on the spinous processes of the second to the seventh thoracic vertebrae through the dorsal scapular ligament. It inserts on the medial surface of the cartilage of the scapula. The serratus dorsalis anterior originates on the lumbar dorsal fascia and dorsal

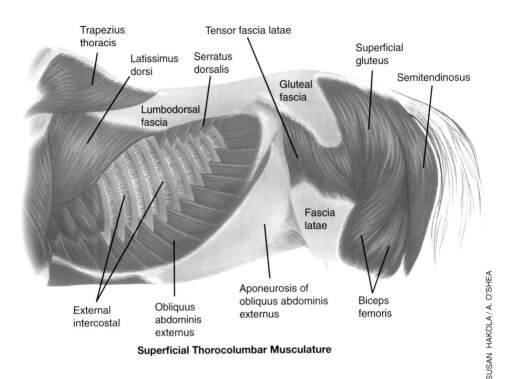

Trapezius thoracis

Latissimus dorsi

Serratus dorsalis

Tensor fascia latae

Gluteal fascia

Superficial gluteus

Semitendinosus

Lumbodorsal fascia

Fascia latae

External intercostal

Obliquus abdominis externus

Aponeurosis of obliquus abdominis externus

Biceps femoris

Superficial Thorocolumbar Musculature

SUSAN HAKOLA / A. O'SHEA

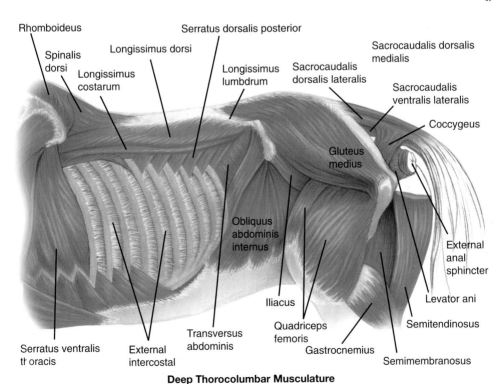

Rhomboideus

Spinalis dorsi

Longissimus costarum

Longissimus dorsi

Serratus dorsalis posterior

Longissimus lumbdrum

Sacrocaudalis dorsalis lateralis

Sacrocaudalis dorsalis medialis

Sacrocaudalis ventralis lateralis

Coccygeus

Gluteus medius

Obliquus abdominis internus

External anal sphincter

Levator ani

Iliacus

Semitendinosus

Serratus ventralis thoracis

External intercostal

Transversus abdominis

Quadriceps femoris

Gastrocnemius

Semimembranosus

Deep Thorocolumbar Musculature

scapular ligament and inserts on the lateral surfaces of the fifth or sixth to the eleventh or twelfth ribs. The serratus dorsalis posterior originates on the lumbar dorsal fascia. It inserts on the lateral surface of the last seven or eight ribs.

The third layer is composed of the longissimus costarum, the longissimus dorsi, the multifidus dorsi, and the intertransversales lumborum.

The *longissimus costarum* muscle originates on the lumbar dorsal fascia around the third or fourth lumbar transverse processes. Its insertion is on the posterior border of the ribs and the transverse processes of the last cervical vertebrae.

The *longissimus dorsi* muscle is the largest and longest muscle in the body. It extends from the sacrum and ilium to the neck, filling up the space between the spinous processes medially and the lumbar transverse processes and upper end of the ribs ventrally. It originates on the ventral surface of the ilium, the first three sacral spines, and the lumbar thoracic

spines of the supraspinous ligament. It inserts on the lumbar transverse and articular processes, the thoracic transverse processes, and the spinous and transverse processes of the last four cervical vertebrae.

The *multifidus dorsi* muscle originates on the lateral part of the sacrum, the articular processes of the lumbar vertebrae, and the transverse processes of the thoracic vertebrae. This muscle inserts on the spinous processes of the first two sacral, the lumbar, the thoracic, and the last cervical vertebrae. The *intertransversales lumborum* occupies the space between the transverse processes of the lumbar vertebrae, except for the fifth and sixth.

The Coccygeal Muscles

This group consists of five pairs of muscles: the *coccygeus*, the *sacral coccygeus dorsalis*, the *sacral coccygeus lateralis, intertransversal caude*, the *sacralcoccygeus ventralis* and the *sacro-coccygeus ventralis*. These muscles all act together to elevate the tail.
℧

Myology is the scientific study of muscles and their accessory structures. Muscle tissues act together to perform work and can be considered the active organs of locomotion or movement. Any movement of the animal's body or its parts is due to muscular contraction. These muscle contractions are in response to neurological stimulation. There are three types of muscle tissue present within the body They are: skeletal muscle (which is striated or striped,) visceral muscles, and cardiac muscles.

In most cases, muscles are attached directly to the bone. However they may be attached to cartilage, ligaments, fascia, or even the skin. The term origin applies to that point of attachment of the muscle which remains more stationary when the muscle contracts. The insertion of the muscle is the more moveable point of attachment. In almost all cases, the attachment is not made by the muscle tissue itself but by fibrous tissue. The term "tendon" is used to indicate a band of dense, white fibrous tissue which attaches the muscle to the bone. The term "aponeurosis" is used when a broad, fibrous sheet facilitates the attachment of the muscle.

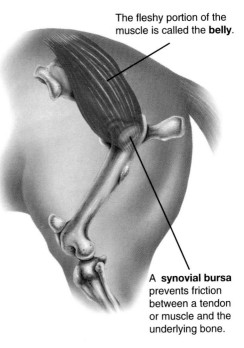

The fleshy portion of the muscle is called the **belly**.

A **synovial bursa** prevents friction between a tendon or muscle and the underlying bone.

The head of the muscle is at the origin of the muscle, whereas the body or fleshy part of the muscle is called the belly. Some muscles are structured with two or more heads and are therefore termed biceps, triceps, etc. A digastric muscle contains two bellies and has a tendon spaced in the center.

Muscle tissue is perfused with circulatory vasculature. Serving this is a very large and elaborate arterial supply and corresponding venous drainage. The muscles are innervated by motor, sensory and vasomotor nerves.

There are two accessory structures associated with the muscle tissues: the synovial membrane and the fascia. The synovial membranes are thin-walled sacks similar to the synovial membranes of the joints. Both structures have a similar function. There are two forms of synovial membranes: the synovial bursa and the synovial sheath. The bursae are located at points that contain unusual amounts of friction or pressure

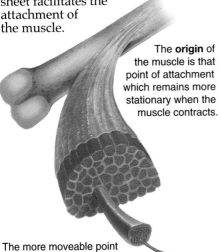

The **origin** of the muscle is that point of attachment which remains more stationary when the muscle contracts.

The more moveable point of attachment of the muscle is called the **insertion**.

SUSAN HAKOLA / J. DIRIG

between a tendon or a muscle and its underlying skeletal structure. A synovial sheath is different from a bursa in that it surrounds a tendon so that two layers can be distinguished. The inner most layer is adherent to the tendon while the outer layer lines the canal in which the tendon lies. The fasciae are sheets of connective tissue that are comprised of bundles of white fibers. These are usually structured in superficial and deep layers.

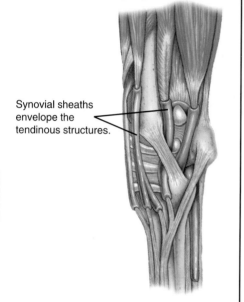

Synovial sheaths envelope the tendinous structures.

The Microscopic Structure of Striated Muscle

Striated muscle fibers are cylindrical in shape and have variable lengths. They are multinucleated with the nuclei being elongated ovoids that are situated in the peripheral cytoplasm of the cylindrically-shaped fibers. Each striated fiber is enclosed by a cell membrane called the sarcolemma. The cross-striated appearance is due to the cytoplasm of the fiber consisting of alternating bands of light and dark material.

Histological staining techniques can further divide the equine skeletal muscle into three major muscle types. These three muscle types differ in their contractility, their oxidative activity, and their ability to store glycogen. They are as follows:

1.) Slow twitch fiber: This is a high oxidative, low glycogen storage fiber that is characterized by its slow speed of contraction. These muscle cells are equipped for aerobic metabolism and show very little fatigue at constant slow speeds. Those animals that have a higher proportion of these types of fibers usually show a better record in endurance events.

2.) Fast twitch fibers: These muscle fibers are called upon when the animal needs a burst of speed. They fatigue rapidly and do not store any appreciable levels of glycogen.

3.) Fast twitch, high oxidative fibers: These muscle fibers resist fatigue better than the fast twitch fibers and can provide bursts of speed for a more sustained period of time. These fibers contain glycogen storage capabilities.

Different breeds of horses will have different proportions of the three types of fibers. Draft horses will contain a larger proportion of slow twitch fibers and fast twitch, high oxidative fibers. Quarter horses, or Thoroughbreds that are involved in sprinting events would have a higher proportion of the fast twitch fibers. The proportion of fast twitch fibers to slow twitch fibers to fast twitch, high oxidative fibers cannot be changed by training. However, training and athletic preparation will increase the size of all three fiber types; therefore, providing a stronger base of those particular fiber types needed for each individual athletic event.

Muscle fibers contain many bundles of myofibrils which are arranged in a parallel fashion.

Myofibrils contain actin and myosin which are depicted as light and dark areas of striation.

The cylindrically-shaped striated muscle fibers are multinucleated and entirely enclosed by the cell membrane or sarcolemma.

Each muscle fiber contains a thousand or more parallel subunits called myofibrils. Lined side by side in each myofibril are thousands of thick and thin myofilaments. The molecular structure of the myofilaments allows an understanding of the mechanism of a muscle contraction.

Myosin, actin, tropomyosin, and troponin are the four different kinds of protein molecules that comprise each myofilament. Thin myofilaments are comprised of a combination of three different proteins. These myofilaments are constructed like strings of beads, with the beads being globular actin molecules, that twist around tropomyosin strands. Actin and myosin molecules have a chemical attraction for one another. At rest, the active sites on the actin molecules are covered up by long tropomyosin molecules. The tropomyosin molecules are held in the blocking

position by troponin molecules spaced in intervals along the thin filaments.

The thick filaments are made almost entirely of myosin molecules. Myosin molecules have a head that sticks out from the filament and a shaft that forms a bundle with other shafts beneath. The myosin heads are chemically attracted to the actin molecules of the nearby thin filaments. Therefore, they angle towards the thin filaments.

The thick and thin filaments alternate within a myofibril. This arrangement allows for contraction of the muscle. The thin filaments attach to both Z lines of a sarcomere and they extend in from the Z lines towards the center of the sarcomere. During relaxation of the muscle fiber, the thin filaments terminate at the outer edges of the H zone. Thick myosin filaments do not attach to the Z lines like the thin filaments. They extend only through

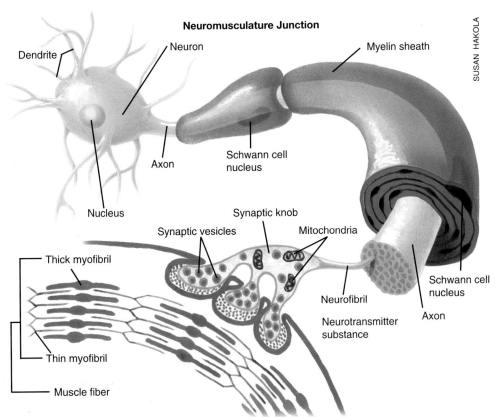

Neuromusculature Junction

Dendrite

Neuron

Myelin sheath

SUSAN HAKOLA

Schwann cell nucleus

Axon

Nucleus

Synaptic knob

Synaptic vesicles

Mitochondria

Thick myofibril

Schwann cell nucleus

Neurofibril

Neurotransmitter substance

Axon

Thin myofibril

Muscle fiber

the length of the A bands of the sarcomeres.

The Neuromuscular Junction

At the distal end of a motor neuron, or nerve cell, there is a chemical junction, or synapse, with the adjacent muscle fiber. As an impulse is transmitted distally through this motor neuron fiber, neurotransmitters (such as acetylcholine) are released from the neuron's synaptic vesicles. These neurotransmitters diffuse across the synaptic cleft where they stimulate receptors in the motor end plate area of the sarcolemma. This stimulation of these acetylcholine receptors initiates an impulse within the sarcolemma. This impulse, which is actually an electrical imbalance, is conducted over the muscle fiber sarcolemma and inward throughout the muscle cell.

Excitation, Contraction and Relaxation

Normally a skeletal muscle fiber is at rest. An entire sequence of events occurs when it is stimulated by a signal or impulse from a special type of nerve cell called the motor neuron. There is an acetylcholine release from the distal end of the motor neuron which stimulates receptor cells and initiates an impulse at the level of the sarcolemma. This diffusion of acetylcholine from the end of the neuron to the muscle fiber itself is called a synaptic reaction.

A temporary electrical imbalance occurs along the muscle fibers sarcolemma with this impulse. The impulse travels through structures called the T tubules to the sacs

of the sarcoplasmic reticulum. The calcium ion is released from the sarcoplasmic reticulum into the sarcoplasm. It is here where the calcium binds with troponin molecules in the thin myofilaments. Tropomyosin molecules in the thin myofilament shift and expose actin's active sites. The next step that occurs in a muscle contraction is that the energized myosin of the thick filaments binds to the actin and utilizes the filament's energy to pull the thin myofilaments to the center of each sarcomere. This cycle repeats itself numerous times as long as there is energy available to the cell. As these thin myofilaments slide past the thick myofilaments, the entire muscle fiber shortens. Therefore, the muscle performs a contraction.

The muscle cell must then relax after it contracts. After the sarcoplasmic reticulum releases the calcium ions into the sarcoplasm, it begins to recover these calcium ions back into the sacs again in anticipation of another impulse. This process only takes a few milliseconds to recover. As the calcium ion is taken from the troponin molecules in the thin myofilaments, tropomyosin returns to its position, again blocking the actin's active sites. Therefore, connection with the myosin is prevented, myosin and actin binding is prohibited, and the muscle can no longer sustain contraction. Since these thick and thin myofilaments are no longer bound, the muscle fiber has to return to its longer resting length. Therefore, it is in a state of relaxation. In summary, the contraction process in a skeletal muscle fiber automatically shuts itself off within a fraction of a second after its initial stimulation from an impulse.

ʊ